Symmetry in Inorganic Chemistry

by

PAUL B. DORAIN

Brandeis University

ADDISON-WESLEY PUBLISHING COMPANY, INC.

READING, MASSACHUSETTS • PALO ALTO • LONDON

This book is in the

ADDISON-WESLEY SERIES IN PRINCIPLES OF CHEMISTRY

FRANCIS T. BONNER

Consulting Editor

Preface

It is now quite apparent that the application of symmetry arguments in the form of group theory is one of the most powerful theoretical tools of the chemist. This book is an attempt to present an introduction to the basic ideas of symmetry and to apply them to inorganic chemistry. In no way is this a rigorous and complete exposition, but it is hoped that an introduction to the use of mathematics in inorganic chemistry at a time when the student is learning the techniques in mathematics courses will help overcome the suspicion and neglect which present students evidence whenever they are confronted by applications to chemistry.

It is assumed that the student has a knowledge of the calculus sufficient for simple differentiation and integration. In addition, some familiarity with the use of vector notation is presupposed. The necessary physics concepts are those of force, energy, and simple electricity and magnetism. It has been unavoidable at some points to introduce an idea without detailed explanation because it would be outside the scope of the book. Depending on the background of a class, it will be necessary at times for additional instruction in these topics. It is hoped that the student will supplement his reading with other texts whenever he is in doubt.

I have almost exclusively used the ideas of electrostatics, particularly in the treatment of coordination compounds. It may be argued that more emphasis should have been given to bond orbitals and ligand field theory. I feel, however, that these concepts should be reserved for a more advanced course in which the foundations of quantum mechanics are carefully exposed. The simple and powerful ideas of Bethe and Van Vleck on crystal field theory are within the understanding of the beginning student and serve as an excellent example of the application of a theory to experiment.

I would like to acknowledge the continual encouragement of Professor Sidney Golden during the writing of this book. In addition, Professors R. W. Kiser of Kansas State University and Francis Bonner of the State University of New York at Stonybrook made many helpful suggestions and comments. I am also grateful to Brandeis University for financial aid in preparing the final typescript.

Waltham, Mass.   P.B.D.
August, 1964

To my wife

Contents

Chapter 5.   **MAGNETIC PROPERTIES OF COORDINATION COMPOUNDS**

1

Crystal Structure

One of the amazing facts of nature is the high degree of symmetry which exists. Indeed, the commonness of symmetry is sufficient reason for most people to ignore the fact. For the scientist, symmetry provides a means to study as a unit a large number of systems which seem unrelated except for this property.

Nowhere is the symmetrical character of nature more apparent than in the natural formations of certain inorganic solids. The appearance of a "good" crystal is that of a solid bounded by plane surfaces. In fact, if two natural crystals of the same material are superficially examined, the impression is that each surface of one crystal has a corresponding surface on the other crystal even though the size and shape may be different. This observation is indeed correct and is a consequence of the internal symmetrical properties of a crystal.

A crystal may be further characterized by performing certain operations. For example if a natural crystal of CaF_2, called fluorite, is crushed into a powder, a microscope reveals that each particle still has plane surfaces which have a simple relationship to the faces of the original crystal. No matter how fine the crystal is ground with ordinary means, each particle is similar to the others. We may infer from this experiment that a crystal is homogeneous in that it is made up of units which are repeated throughout the crystal.

A crystal is also anisotropic. If a natural crystal of halite, NaCl, is cleaved with a razor blade, it is found that it is very easy to obtain plane surfaces which are at right angles to each other, but it is almost impossible to obtain a cleavage at some acute angle to one of these surfaces.

There are many other experiments which may be performed which serve to show that a crystal is a homogeneous, anisotropic condensed phase of matter.

THE LAW OF RATIONAL INDICES

It was mentioned in the introduction that a visual examination of a number of crystals of a given mineral creates the impression that the crystals have similarities. This fact led Nicolaus Steno in 1669 to measure the angles between the faces of quartz crystals. He found that no matter how the crystal was cut and distorted the corresponding angles between faces were always the same.

A way of presenting these data for a given crystal is to place the crystal at the center of a large sphere. If all radii which are perpendicular to the faces of the crystal are noted on the surface of the sphere, then it is found that the points of intersection for crystals of the same mineral are identical. An example of this projection is shown in Fig. 1–1(a).

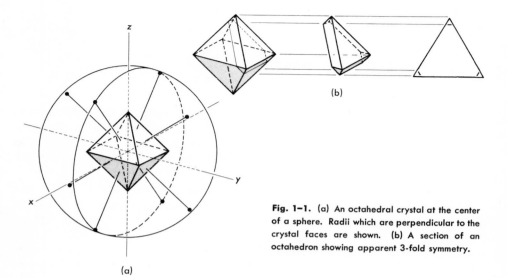

Fig. 1–1. (a) An octahedral crystal at the center of a sphere. Radii which are perpendicular to the crystal faces are shown. (b) A section of an octahedron showing apparent 3-fold symmetry.

(a)

It is convenient to reduce the complexity of the drawing by making a stereographic projection on a plane of the points on the sphere in the following manner. All points in the northern hemisphere are joined to the south pole by lines and all points in the southern hemisphere are joined to the north pole. The intersections of the lines with the equatorial plane are marked by dots for those lines coming from the south pole and circles for those coming from the north pole. The projection of the crystal in Fig. 1–1(a) is shown in Fig. 1–2.

If a section of a regular octahedron is considered as shown in Fig. 1–1(b), then the faces may be extended or the angular measurements between faces can be made to give an identical stereoprojection to that obtained from a regular octahedron. Such a projection shows symmetry which may not be obviously present in the crystal itself. The section of the octahedron in Fig. 1–1(b) appears to have only symmetries involving rotation by $2\pi/3$, but angular measurements put the crystal into a class with rotational symmetry of $\pi/2$. In fact, all crystals may be classified according to their symmetry by the above procedure.

A consequence of the constancy of angles between faces of a crystal is that any face may be represented by three numbers or indices, h_1, h_2, h_3, which are in the ratio of small integers. This empirical law was discovered by Renee Haüy in about 1780 and is referred to as the law of rational indices. The numbers are called Miller indices.

To understand the meaning of rational indices, it is convenient to examine a two-dimensional rather than a real three-dimensional crystal. A sheet of mica or graphite approximates this situation. An edge in a two-dimensional lattice corresponds to a face in a three-dimensional case. It may be represented by an equation for a straight line which in a perpendicular coordinate system whose

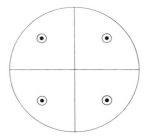

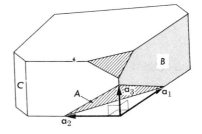

Fig. 1–2. A stereographic projection of Fig. 1–1(a).

Fig. 1–3. A crystal with a possible choice of unit vectors. These vectors are normal to each other.

unit vectors are $\mathbf{a}_1$ and $\mathbf{a}_2$ is

$$x_1 = mx_2 + b. \tag{1–1}$$

The slope of the line is m, b is the $\mathbf{a}_2$-axis intercept, and x_1 and x_2 are the number of unit lengths of $\mathbf{a}_1$ and $\mathbf{a}_2$. Any other line parallel to this line has the same slope m but a different intercept. We could have written the equation in the alternative form

$$h_1x_1 + h_2x_2 - C = 0, \tag{1–2}$$

where now the $\mathbf{a}_1$ intercept is C/h_1 and the $\mathbf{a}_2$ intercept is C/h_2. The ratio of the intercepts, h_2/h_1, is a constant for any value of C and is just the negative of the slope of the line.

For a three-dimensional crystal, the equation of a plane is just the extension of the two-dimensional case and is given by

$$h_1x_1 + h_2x_2 + h_3x_3 - C = 0. \tag{1–3}$$

A plane parallel to any other plane has the same ratio of $h_1:h_2:h_3$, but of course C will differ.

A scheme for determining the indices of faces for a real crystal is as follows: Three noncoplanar edges of the crystal are chosen. These edges form three vectors which intersect at a point called the origin of the system. In general, these vectors will not be at right angles. To fix the length of the vectors, a face is chosen which intersects all three axes. Arbitrarily we may choose the ratio $h_1:h_2:h_3$ to be $1:1:1$. That is, the unit length of each vector is the distance from the origin to the intersection with this plane. Such a plane is labeled A in Fig. 1–3. Once this is done any other plane may be represented by three integers. A plane such as B in Fig. 1–3 is the $(0, 1, 0)$ plane since $C/h_1 = \infty$, $C/h_2 = 1$, and $C/h_3 = \infty$. The reciprocals are in the ratio of $0:1:0$. A negative index is denoted by a bar over the index. For instance, plane C is the $(\bar{1}, 1, 0)$ plane. For nonorthogonal axes, the problem becomes more complicated because of the necessity to use vector algebra, but the basic construction of the Miller indices for a crystal face remains the same.

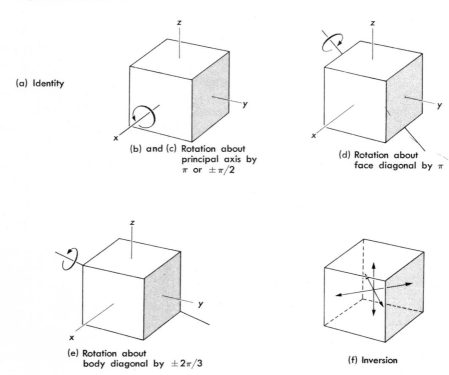

(a) Identity

(b) and (c) Rotation about principal axis by π or $\pm\pi/2$

(d) Rotation about face diagonal by π

(e) Rotation about body diagonal by $\pm 2\pi/3$

(f) Inversion

Fig. 1–4. The symmetry operations of a cube.

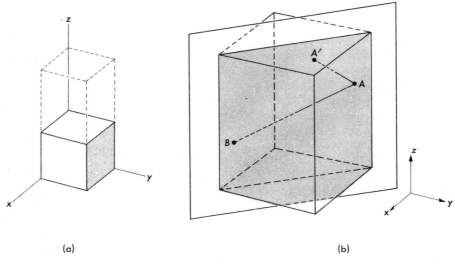

(a)

(b)

Fig. 1–5. (a) The elongation of a cube to produce a tetragonal prism. (b) A tetragonal prism showing the equivalence of reflection symmetry and rotation-inversion symmetry.

SYMMETRY

In the previous section, the symmetrical nature of the faces of a crystal was shown to be clearly evident from a stereographic projection. For the octahedral crystal, the stereographic projection is repeated if it is rotated by 0, $\pi/2$, π, or $3\pi/2$ about an axis perpendicular to the figure passing through point O. This axis of rotation is called a 4-fold axis of symmetry. There are additional symmetry operations. For instance, a reflection in a plane which bisects the angle between the lines shown in Fig. 1–2 is a symmetry operation. All the symmetry operations for a figure may be enumerated and such a collection is called the symmetry group of the figure.

As an example, consider the symmetry operations of a cube. In Fig. 1–4, a cube is oriented with the x-, y-, and z-axes parallel to the cube edges. The symmetry operations or, as they are commonly called, symmetry elements are

(a) no operation, the identity operation;

(b) rotations about x, y, or z by $\pm\pi/2$; six operations or elements;

(c) rotations about x, y, or z by π; three elements;

(d) rotation about the face diagonals by π; six elements;

(e) rotations about the body diagonals by $\pm 2\pi/3$; eight elements.

The total number of elements is 24. A possible additional symmetry is the inversion operation which corresponds to moving every point (x_i, y_i, z_i) of the cube through the origin to the point $(-x_i, -y_i, -z_i)$. The inclusion of inversion symmetry doubles the number of elements because each operation listed previously may be followed by inversion, giving a new symmetry position. Thus the total number of symmetry elements of a cube is 48.

If the cube is distorted by elongating the edges parallel to the z-axis, as shown in Fig. 1–5(a), the number of symmetry elements is reduced. If inversion is ignored, the eight symmetry operations are

(a) identity;

(b) rotation about z by $\pm\pi/2$; two elements;

(c) rotation about x, y, or z by π; three elements;

(d) rotation about base diagonals by π; two elements.

It may be argued that the cube and rectangular parallelepiped also have planes of symmetry. For example, in Fig. 1–5(b) a plane of symmetry is shown which is parallel to the z-axis of the rectangular parallelepiped or tetragonal prism. A point such as A becomes A' upon reflection in the plane. But it is also possible to change A into A' by inversion followed by a rotation. That is, inversion changes A to B. A rotation by π about y and a rotation by $\pi/2$ about z brings B to A'. In general, any reflection operation is a product of an inversion and a rotation operation.

It is not necessary to consider only geometrical objects to discuss symmetry. In fact, a useful mathematical tool of scientists is the application of **symmetry** to mathematical functions. Consider the following second-degree functions of x, y, and z: $x^2 - y^2$, z^2, xy, xz, and yz where $x^2 + y^2 + z^2 = 1$. Under the symmetry group of the tetragonal prism the following transformations of the x, y, and z coordinates occur:

(a) identity; $x \to x$, $y \to y$, $z \to z$;

(b) rotation about z by $\pi/2$; $x \to y$, $y \to -x$, $z \to z$;

(c) rotation about z by π; $x \to -x$, $y \to -y$, $z \to z$;

(d) rotation about y by π; $x \to -x$, $y \to y$, $z \to -z$.

The other operations of each type do not need to be considered since they are similar to the ones given. It is seen that the functions are transformed by these operations as follows:

$$z^2 \to z^2,$$
$$x^2 - y^2 \to x^2 - y^2, \qquad \text{for all transformations;}$$
$$xy \to \pm xy,$$

$$\begin{aligned} xz &\to yz, \\ yz &\to -xz, \end{aligned} \qquad \text{for transformation } b;$$

$$\begin{aligned} xz &\to -xz, \\ yz &\to -yz, \end{aligned} \qquad \text{for transformation } c;$$

$$\begin{aligned} xz &\to +xz, \\ yz &\to -yz, \end{aligned} \qquad \text{for transformation } d.$$

Thus, z^2, $x^2 - y^2$, and xy transform only into themselves and are said to possess the symmetry of the group. On the other hand, xz and yz are transformed into each other or the negative of each other by the group operations. Only when they are considered as a pair do they have the group symmetry. Such a pair is called a degenerate set of functions.

UNIT CELLS

It might be imagined that a crystal which has certain facial symmetry may be cleaved along the planes until a solid is obtained which, if cleaved further, will not show the symmetry of the original crystal. Note that the requirement of this unit of volume, V, is that it possess the symmetry of the crystal, and by stacking n units together a crystal of volume nV is obtained. Such a unit volume may be described by three vectors, $\mathbf{a}_1$, $\mathbf{a}_2$, $\mathbf{a}_3$, whose volume is the scalar triple product, $(\mathbf{a}_1 \cdot \mathbf{a}_2 \times \mathbf{a}_3)$. Any point in a given unit volume or *unit cell* has a corresponding point in another unit cell. The displacement vector or distance vector from one unit cell to another is given by

$$\mathbf{L} = n_1\mathbf{a}_1 + n_2\mathbf{a}_2 + n_3\mathbf{a}_3, \tag{1-4}$$

where n_1, n_2, and n_3 are integers. Thus any point in a given unit cell represented by a vector $\mathbf{R}$ has a corresponding point in another cell given by the vector, $\mathbf{L} + \mathbf{R}$.

One may ask how many ways the three unit vectors can be chosen. To answer this question, it is convenient to use a two-dimensional lattice again. In this case two unit vectors are needed to define a plane figure which when repeated fills a plane completely. We could guess that squares may be used as one unit cell since they may be repeated to fill a plane, but pentagons do not fit properly together, as shown in Fig. 1–6(a).

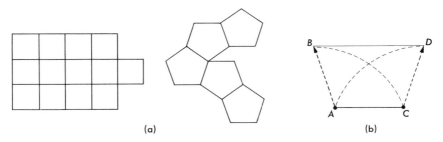

Fig. 1–6. (a) The packing of squares leaves no empty space, whereas the packing of pentagons leaves holes. (b) The effect of rotating about two equivalent n-fold points by $+2\pi/n$ and $-2\pi/n$ radians.

The two vectors we chose will determine the symmetry of the unit cell. To obtain the allowed symmetry we may assume that one vector is the distance from A to C in Fig. 1–6(b). In addition we assume that axes of n-fold symmetry pass through points A and C where n is to be determined. Let us rotate about A by $2\pi/n$ radians, which sends point C to point B. A similar rotation of $-2\pi/n$ radians about C sends point A to point D. Three cases are of interest. The points B and D may coincide, the distance $\overline{BD}$ may be equal to the distance $\overline{AC}$, or else $\overline{BD} > \overline{AC}$. The requirement that the unit cell be the smallest unit plane which still has the proper symmetry forces the distance $\overline{AC}$, the length of the unit vector, to be equal to or less than any other distance to an axis of n-fold symmetry. If B and D coincide, n must be 6, and if $\overline{BD} = \overline{AC}$, $n = 4$. For $\overline{BD} = 2\overline{AC}$, $n = 3$, but for any other length of $\overline{BD} > \overline{AC}$, $n = 2$. Therefore the unit cells may have only 2-, 3-, 4-, or 6-fold symmetry.

The lengths of the two vectors are either equal or nonequal. If they are equal, then the unit cells are equilateral parallelograms, squares, or hexagons, corresponding to 2-, 4-, or 3- and 6-fold symmetry. If unequal vectors are used either a parallelepiped or a rectangle is the unit cell. These unit cells in their lattices are illustrated in Fig. 1–7. No other unit cells are possible for a plane.

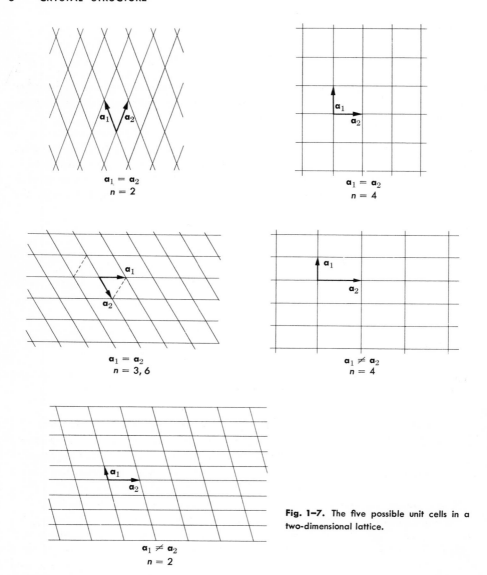

Fig. 1–7. The five possible unit cells in a two-dimensional lattice.

Since a three-dimensional lattice is a simple extension of a two-dimensional lattice, the same rotational restrictions must hold. However, the number of possible unit cells increases from five to six because of the combinations of rotational symmetry about different axes.

In three dimensions the unit cells are defined by three vectors, a_1, a_2, a_3, and all the possible polyhedra may be constructed with this vector set subject to the symmetry restrictions of 1-, 2-, 3-, 4-, or 6-fold rotational symmetry. The six solids so constructed are shown in Fig. 1–8. For each figure, the angle between each pair of vectors is given as well as the vectors. All known crystals

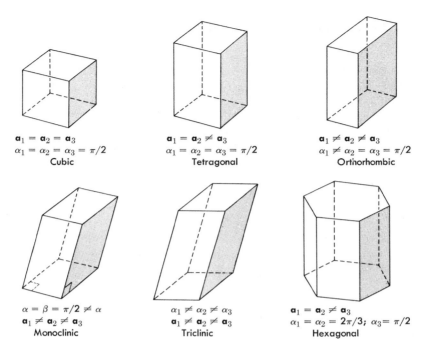

$a_1 = a_2 = a_3$
$\alpha_1 = \alpha_2 = \alpha_3 = \pi/2$
Cubic

$a_1 = a_2 \neq a_3$
$\alpha_1 = \alpha_2 = \alpha_3 = \pi/2$
Tetragonal

$a_1 \neq a_2 \neq a_3$
$\alpha_1 \neq \alpha_2 = \alpha_3 = \pi/2$
Orthorhombic

$\alpha = \beta = \pi/2 \neq \alpha$
$a_1 \neq a_2 \neq a_3$
Monoclinic

$\alpha_1 \neq \alpha_2 \neq \alpha_3$
$a_1 \neq a_2 \neq a_3$
Triclinic

$a_1 = a_2 \neq a_3$
$\alpha_1 = \alpha_2 = 2\pi/3; \; \alpha_3 = \pi/2$
Hexagonal

Fig. 1–8. The six crystal systems.

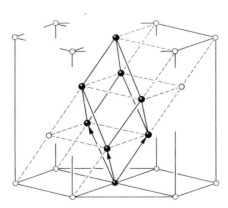

Fig. 1–9. A diagram showing the equivalence of the rhombohedral crystal system to the hexagonal system.

may be classified according to the particular unit cell which makes up the crystal. These classifications are called the six crystal systems.

It may be argued that there is, in addition to these figures, the possibility of $a_1 = a_2 = a_3$ and $\alpha_1 = \alpha_2 = \alpha_3 \neq \pi/2$. However, the rhombohedron so formed can be placed in the hexagonal system. The construction is shown in Fig. 1–9; or by the use of symmetry operations the student can show that the rhombohedron has a 6-fold axis of rotation-inversion.

THE INTERNAL STRUCTURE OF CRYSTALS

Up to now, any discussion of the atomic nature of crystals has been avoided. But, for the chemist, this is the more important information. Prior to the turn of the century, there was no method which gave this information directly. In Germany in 1912, Von Laue, Friedrich, and Knipping scattered a beam of x-rays from a crystal. At the time it was suspected but not known that x-rays were electromagnetic. It was also suspected that atoms in a crystal had repeated arrangements. The three physicists in this one experiment demonstrated that both suppositions were indeed correct. The nature of the experimental determination of structure by x-rays will be given in Chapter 2.

The first consequence of a periodic arrangement of molecules or atoms in a crystal is an explanation of the law of rational indices. In Fig. 1–10 a two-dimensional crystal is drawn with dots to represent atoms. Growth of the crystal generally occurs perpendicular to a row of atoms because each atom will be acted on by attractive forces from several other atoms. Thus an incoming atom will be less likely to bind to a single atom to form a "spike" than to bind to several atoms along a row.

Edges A and B may be used to define two vectors, a_1 and a_2, whose unit length is defined by edge C and the intersection of the vectors at O. Another edge possibility for the crystal is edge D. The intercepts of this edge are 6.5 and 3.25 unit lengths. Therefore, this edge is the (2, 1) edge. If an edge existed at line E, the intercepts would be (3, 12) and thus have a ratio of $\frac{1}{4}$. This example illustrates that the rational indices will have ratios of whole numbers. Since the probability is small that a face will develop during growth with the atoms which form the edge being far from each other, the Miller indices are *small* integers.

The second consequence of the periodicity of atoms in crystals is the description of the interior of the unit cell. Previously the unit cell had been described as resulting from a process of reducing the size of a crystal by cleaving it along planes until the smallest unit was obtained which could still be repeated to fill all space. However, the periodic arrangement of atoms affords a better picture of the idea of a unit cell.

The student can imagine himself placed at some point in the interior of the crystal. He examines the symmetry of his surroundings very carefully. Then he moves in the crystal until he finds another symmetrically identical position. A vector is chosen to be the line from the original point to one which has identical symmetry. The student returns to the original point and defines two additional vectors by finding two other points with identical symmetry. The vectors must not be coplanar. Clearly, these three vectors describe a unit cell which can be stacked together to fill all space.

What are the characteristics of this unit cell? First, the unit cell is not unique because any finite crystal contains a very large number of atoms, and numerous identical points may be found. Of course, it is possible to find the smallest unit cell and more important the smallest unit cell with maximum symmetry.

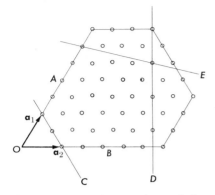

Fig. 1-10. A two-dimensional crystal illustrating the law of rational indices.

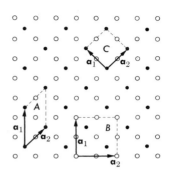

Fig. 1-11. Three possible unit cells for a two-dimensional lattice. Cell C is the primitive cell.

One of the more convenient points at which a vector may originate in a crystal is an atom. Then the vector terminations are on atoms also. In Fig. 1–11, a two-dimensional crystal is drawn which shows three possible unit cells. Unit cell A has 2-fold symmetry and, as can be counted from Fig. 1–11, has two circles and one dot per unit cell if fractional atoms are counted at the corners and edges. Cell B has more symmetry but also is larger since it contains four circles and two dots. Cell C has two circles and a dot per unit cell as in cell A, but it also has maximum symmetry since it has a 4-fold axis. Frequently the smallest unit cell does not have the maximum symmetry. In this case the unit cell is chosen on the basis of convenience which generally means that the cell with maximum symmetry is chosen. The cell with the smallest volume is called the primitive unit cell.

For three dimensions, the same considerations apply. Figure 1–12(a) shows a NaCl structure with the primitive cell outlined as well as the smallest and most symmetrical unit cell. In Fig. 1–12(b), a crystal model of the zinc blende struc-

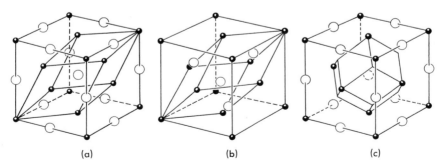

(a)   (b)   (c)

Fig. 1-12. (a) The sodium chloride unit cell with smallest volume and maximum symmetry. The primitive unit cell is outlined in this cell. (b) The zinc blende unit cells showing maximum symmetry case and primitive cell. Note the similarity to the NaCl lattice. (c) The Wigner-Seitz unit cell for NaCl.

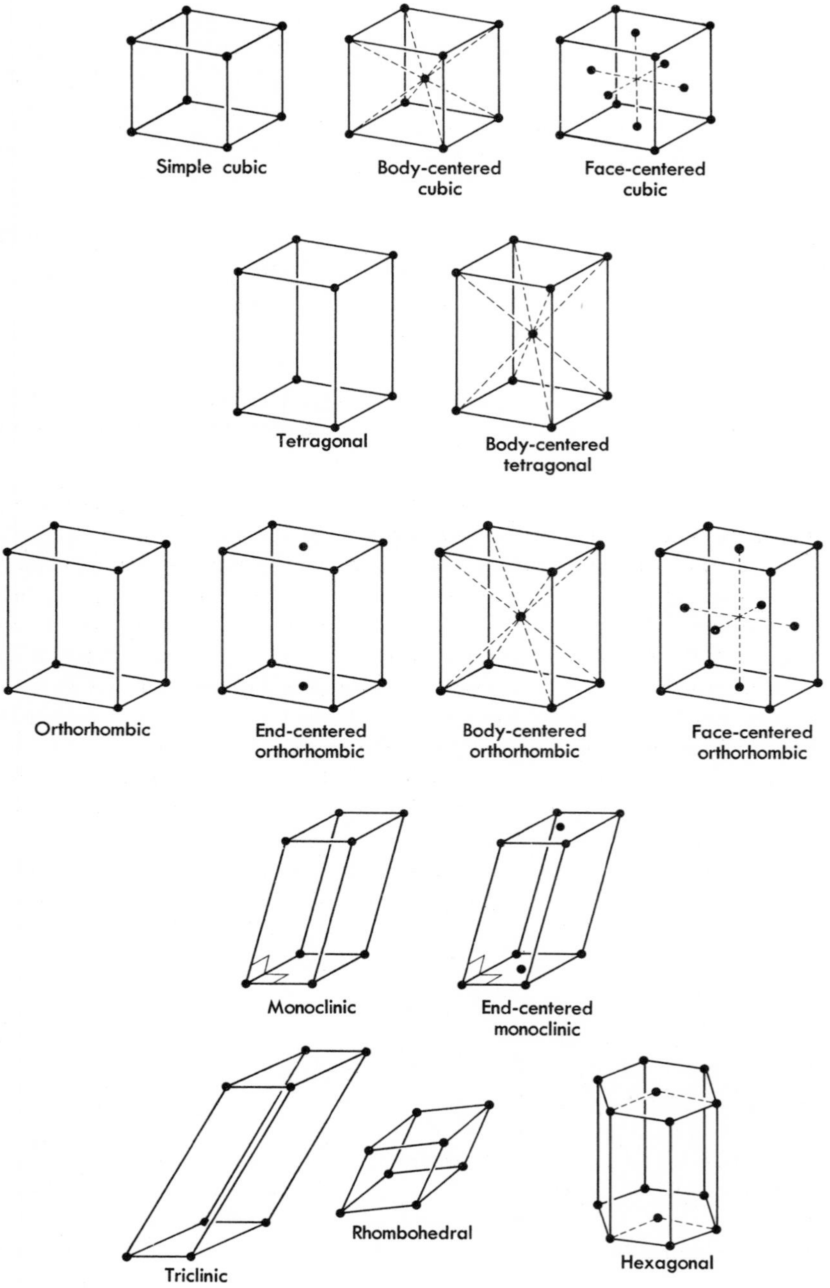

Fig. 1–13. The fourteen Bravais lattices.

ture is drawn. It is also cubic as can be seen from the smallest unit cell with maximum symmetry. The primitive unit cell is a rhombohedron as is NaCl, but the cell now lacks inversion symmetry because the interior atom is not centrally located.

The third result of the atomic periodicity of the crystal lattice is the division of crystal structures into 14 lattice types depending upon the symmetry of the unit cell and the translations necessary to get to an equivalent point in the unit cell. These lattice types are called the Bravais lattices or space lattices and are shown in Fig. 1–13.

In space lattices, the idea of a translation along a vector is introduced to get to an equivalent point in the unit cell. Such a vector is called a nonprimitive translation. As an example, in a body-centered cubic cell, the body centers have the same symmetry as the corners of the unit cells. To go from a corner to a body center, a nonprimitive translation vector is defined which in terms of the primitive vectors is given by $\frac{1}{2}\mathbf{a}_1 + \frac{1}{2}\mathbf{a}_2 + \frac{1}{2}\mathbf{a}_3$.

After examining Fig. 1–13, it might appear that several possibilities of space lattices have been omitted, but by inspection it is seen that each omitted lattice can be constructed from one of the 14 Bravais lattices. For example, a face-centered tetragonal lattice is missing from the list, but Fig. 1–14 shows that the face-centered and body-centered tetragonal structures are identical.

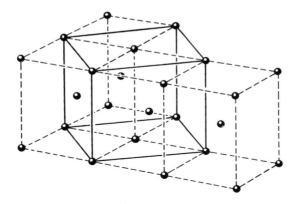

Fig. 1–14. An illustration of the equivalence of the face-centered and body-centered tetragonal structures.

The method described above to obtain a unit cell is not the only way unit cells are defined. For example, if a volume is formed from all points closer to a given point than to any other identical point, then this volume forms a unit cell. Such a unit cell for the NaCl lattice is shown in Fig. 1–12(c). It is not obvious that such a solid can fill space, but one of Euclid's contributions was to show that this dodecahedron is one of five regular polyhedra which can fill all space. It should be noted that this figure has the symmetry of a cube. Such a unit cell is called a Wigner-Seitz cell and is useful in solid-state physics.

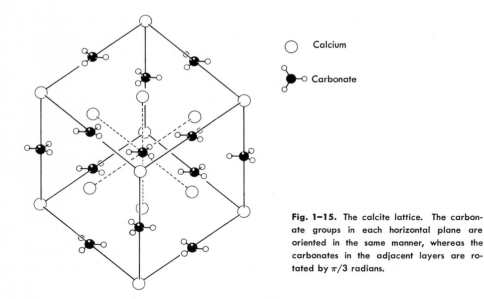

Calcium

Carbonate

Fig. 1–15. The calcite lattice. The carbonate groups in each horizontal plane are oriented in the same manner, whereas the carbonates in the adjacent layers are rotated by $\pi/3$ radians.

The question now arises as to how many different symmetry patterns can be placed in each Bravais lattice. Figure 1–12 shows two face-centered cubic unit cells, but each has different internal symmetry. As mentioned above, the zinc blende cell lacks inversion symmetry whereas the sodium chloride cell has a center of symmetry. A more complicated lattice is that of calcite, a single crystal of $CaCO_3$. The Ca^{2+} and CO_3^{2-} ions are arranged in a distorted cubic cell. The distortion is a compression along one of the $(1, 1, 1)$ axes. Figure 1–15 shows a model of the lattice where it can be seen that each CO_3^{2-} ion has 3-fold symmetry. The Bravais lattice is hexagonal. Each CO_3^{2-} ion in a given layer has the same orientation, but the carbonate ions in the nearest neighbor layers are rotated by $\pi/3$. Thus the symmetry operations which relate the CO_3^{2-} ions must include both a nonprimitive translation and rotation. Such operations are sometimes described as screw axes and glide planes. Clearly, the symmetry is more complicated in calcite than in sodium chloride and it might seem that there is an infinite number of possible combinations of Bravais lattices with the internal or point symmetries. Actually, the number of such combinations may be enumerated theoretically. The 230 symmetry groups obtained are called the three-dimensional space groups.

METALLIC AND INERT GAS CRYSTALS

In metals and in crystals of condensed inert gases, such as argon, neon, or krypton, the forces between atoms have no directional properties. Therefore, we can approximate an atom as a spherical solid body. The crystal structures may be considered as the result of packing spheres in the most economical pat-

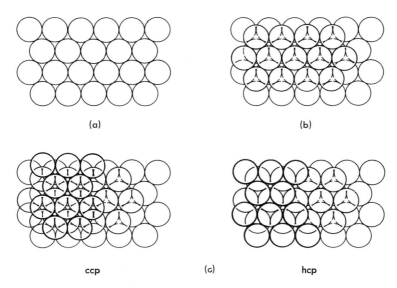

(a)   (b)

ccp   (c)   hcp

Fig. 1–16. The hexagonal close-packing and cubic close-packing of spheres.

terns. As we shall see, there are an infinite number of ways to satisfy the criterion, but fortunately most metals and all inert gases crystallize in only two ways, either hexagonal close-packing or cubic close-packing.

Figure 1–16(a) shows the only way spheres can be closely packed in a plane. This pattern is the same as that assumed by soap bubbles on a liquid surface although they obviously are not hard spheres. A second layer of spheres may be placed over the holes of the first layer, as shown in Fig. 1–16(b). It should be noted that the spheres from the second layer cover only half of the holes of the first layer. Therefore, in adding the third layer of spheres, two choices are available: either (1) the third-layer spheres lie over the first-layer spheres, or (2) the third-layer spheres lie over the remaining holes of the first layer. If the first layer is called A and the second layer, B, then it is possible to repeat layer A or have a different layer C. Clearly, structures of the type $ABABAB \ldots$ and $ABCABCABC \ldots$ are possible. But it is also possible to have an infinite number of structures of which one example is $ABABCABABCABABC \ldots$. The scheme $ABAB \ldots$ has at most 6-fold symmetry and, therefore, falls into the hexagonal system. The sequence $ABCABC \ldots$ is a cubic arrangement. The unit cell is outlined in Fig. 1–17, which shows that the cell is face-centered cubic. As was previously stated, it is fortunate that most crystals which can be treated as the packing of spheres have either the hexagonal or cubic close-packing arrangement. An example of a cubic close-packing (ccp) structure is that of silver, whereas zinc has the hexagonal close-packing (hcp) arrangement. Among some materials like nickel and calcium, difficulty arises in deciding the arrangement of crystallization. The arrangement may be $ABABABCBCBCB \ldots$. Such a change is called a stacking fault.

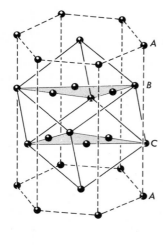

Fig. 1–17. The face-centered unit cell of a cubic close-packed arrangement of spheres.

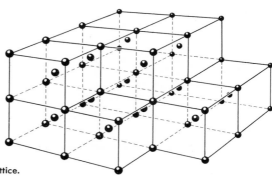

Fig. 1–18. The body-centered cubic lattice.

Each atom for a close-packed arrangement has twelve nearest neighbors, six in a plane containing the atom and three above and below this plane. It is apparent that the particular arrangement depends not on the interaction with nearest neighbors but upon next nearest neighbor forces. For most elements, interaction forces decrease rapidly with separation.* Consequently, transitions from one form to the other occur as the temperature or pressure is changed.

A third common crystal form for metallic crystals is the body-centered structure (bcc). This structure is shown in Fig. 1–18, where it can be seen that each atom is surrounded by eight nearest neighbors and six additional atoms which are only 14% more distant than the nearest neighbors. As an example, the alkali metals crystallize in this structure. There are two atoms per unit cell with the coordinates $(0, 0, 0)$ and $(\frac{1}{2}, \frac{1}{2}, \frac{1}{2})$ where the three vectors are chosen to give a unit cell with cubic symmetry.

---

* Two terms are generally found in the literature to designate the forces between bodies. The so-called short-range forces are those which decrease rapidly with the separation distance. Long-range forces are those which are effective over longer distances. Since a force is related to the gradient of the potential energy of a system by $\mathbf{F} = -\nabla U$, we may alternatively speak of the potential energy variation. For example, a long-range force is the coulombic interaction between two point charges, since the force varies as $1/r^2$ and the potential energy as $-1/r$. A short-range force arises in the case of dipole-dipole interaction where the average potential energy goes as $1/r^6$. The so-called van der Waals forces, which are the main contributions to the interaction between neutral atoms and molecules, result from all potentials which vary as $1/r^6$.

The bcc arrangement is not a close-packed arrangement. This fact is emphasized by calculating the ratio of the volume occupied by the spheres in a unit cell to the volume of the unit cell. For a bcc lattice the fraction is 0.68 which may be compared with 0.74 for the close-packed model. Nevertheless, it is not very different so that subtle changes in energy between each atom and its nearest neighbors cause a metal to crystallize in one form or the other.

PACKING ARRANGEMENTS FOR ATOMS OF DIFFERENT SIZES

If the atoms in a solid of composition AB are of different sizes then the ratio of the radii of atom A to the radius of atom B is important in determining the packing arrangement. Consider a tetrahedral arrangement with atom A surrounded by four B-atoms as shown in Fig. 1–19. The radius ratio may be calculated for the condition that the B-atoms just touch. A tetrahedron may be placed in a cube of edge a with atoms B placed in opposite corners and the A-atom in the center. The distance $\overline{BB}$ is equal to $2r_B$, where r_B is the radius of the atom B, and the distance from A to B is $r_A + r_B$. From geometry:

$$r_B = (\sqrt{2}/2)a,$$
$$r_A + r_B = (\sqrt{3}/2)a, \qquad (1\text{–}5)$$
$$r_A/r_B = \frac{\sqrt{3} - \sqrt{2}}{\sqrt{2}} = 0.225.$$

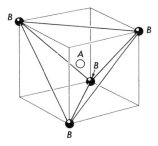

Fig. 1–19. A tetrahedral arrangement of B-atoms surrounding an A-type atom.

Thus a ccp or hcp arrangement of B atoms will not be disturbed if an atom of type A is inserted in an interstitial position provided the radius ratio of A to B is less than 0.225. For a bcc lattice the critical radius ratio is 0.732.

IONIC CRYSTALS

The ionic crystal structures might be expected to differ from those resulting from the packing of neutral spheres because coulombic forces are involved. The potential due to an ion of charge Ze is Ze^2/r, where r is the distance from the ion to the point at which the potential is measured. It is clear that this potential has spherical symmetry and falls off as $1/r$, whereas for inert gas molecules, the potentials from van der Waals forces vary as $1/r^6$. Otherwise, we may expect that the ions behave like spheres and will have a tendency to pack, as discussed above.

Sodium chloride crystallizes into a face-centered cubic lattice of chloride ions with the sodium ions forming another face-centered cubic lattice displaced from

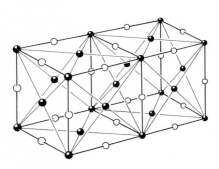

Fig. 1–20. The NaCl lattice.

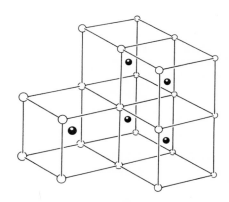

Fig. 1–21. The CsCl lattice.

the chloride lattice by the vector $(\frac{1}{2}, \frac{1}{2}, \frac{1}{2})$. This arrangement is the simplest of ionic crystal structures, and all materials which have this structure are said to crystallize in the NaCl lattice. Figure 1–20 illustrates the lattice.

Cesium chloride does not crystallize into the NaCl lattice except under special conditions, but crystallizes with the lattice shown in Fig. 1–21. This lattice is a simple cubic lattice of cations or anions with the anion lattice displaced from the cation lattice by the vector $(\frac{1}{2}, \frac{1}{2}, \frac{1}{2})$. The only alkali halide crystals with this form are CsCl, CsBr, CsI, and, under high pressure, RbCl, RbBr, and RbI.

An ionic structure similar to that of CsCl is the CaF_2 or fluorite structure. The fluorite structure is shown in Fig. 1–22, where it can be seen that the difference between it and CsCl is that every other cation position in the CsCl structure is missing in the fluorite lattice. The structure is a face-centered cubic lattice.

Unlike the NaCl lattice, the fluorite lattice affords an opportunity to illustrate a cubic cell which involves translational symmetry. If the unit cell in Fig. 1–22 is rotated by $\pm\pi/2$ about the z-axis, then all the fluorides are rotated into positions occupied by fluorides before the rotation. However, the calcium ions are now in positions where previously there were no ions. To obtain the original lattice a rotation by $\pi/2$ must be followed by a translation of the type $(\frac{1}{2}, 0, 0)$. Thus CaF_2, although it is cubic, belongs to a different space group than CsCl.

One additional illustration of a common ionic lattice is the rutile lattice, which is illustrated in Fig. 1–23. MgF_2 and SnO_2 are examples of compounds which crystallize in this form. Each cation has six nearest anions, and each anion has three nearest cations. The unit cell is tetragonal.

There are many ionic lattices of salts which consist of a simple cation and a complicated anion, or vice versa. The structures of these salts are frequently one of those described above with the complex ion assuming the position in the lattice of the simple ion of the same charge. An example of such a salt is K_2ReCl_6 which is a face-centered cubic lattice of potassium ions and $ReCl_6^{2-}$ ions. The

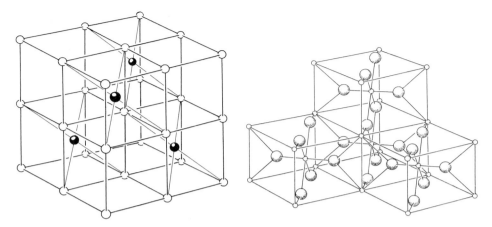

Fig. 1–22. The fluorite or calcium fluoride lattice.   **Fig. 1–23.** The rutile lattice.

space group is the same as fluorite except that the positions of anions and cations are interchanged. In this crystal a large cation is necessary to fill the space left by the packing of the complex anion in order to maintain the cubic lattice.

IONIC RADII AND THE LATTICE ENERGY

It is convenient for the chemist to have some indication of the size of ions in crystals in order to predict structure of other crystals or to ascertain whether an ion will fit into an interstitial position of a lattice. To give a definite size to an ion is an approximation because quantum-mechanical calculations can give only a probability for finding an electron in a volume element, $d\tau$. As a consequence an arbitrary method has been derived by crystallographers to give an estimate of an ionic radius.

As will be shown later, x-ray information gives lattice spacings between equivalent planes. In a crystal of KCl, the spacing between the (100) planes is 6.28 A. Since this is a K—Cl—K or Cl—K—Cl distance, it may be halved to give the KCl distance as 3.14 A. The question now is whether or not meaningful ionic radii may be extracted from this measurement.

From the quantum-mechanical analysis of the hydrogen atom, the radius for the electron with a principal quantum number n is given by

$$r = \frac{n^2\hbar^2}{mZe^2}, \qquad n = 1, 2, 3 \ldots, \tag{1-6}$$

where $\hbar$ is Planck's constant divided by 2π, m is the mass of the electron, e is an electron charge unit, and Ze is the nuclear charge. If it is assumed that the outer electrons are responsible for the size of the ion, then it may be further assumed that these electrons are attracted to the nucleus by the charge Ze except for the screening of this charge by the inner electrons. The effective charge may be written as $(Z - S)e$, where S is a screening constant. The radius may then be written as

$$r_{\text{ion}} = \frac{N}{Z - S}, \tag{1-7}$$

where N is a constant composed of all the constants in Eq. (1-6) including a given principal quantum number.

Screening constants may be calculated by using a set of rules given by J. C. Slater* or may be obtained from values of mole refraction and x-ray term values. For ions with the neon configuration, S is 4.52 per electron charge, and for argon it is 11.25 per electron charge. Using Eq. (1-7) and the internuclear distance for KCl, we find

$$r_{\text{K}^+} + r_{\text{Cl}^-} = 3.14 \text{ A},$$

$$\frac{r_{\text{K}^+}}{r_{\text{Cl}^-}} = \frac{17 - 11.25}{19 - 11.25}, \tag{1-8}$$

$$r_{\text{K}^+} = 1.33 \text{ A}, \qquad r_{\text{Cl}^-} = 1.81 \text{ A}.$$

Similar calculations may be made for all alkali halides.

It might be expected that CaS, which has the NaCl structure, could be treated in the same manner. The measured internuclear distance is 2.84 A. Using our radius of K^+ we find

$$\frac{r_{\text{Ca}^{2+}}}{r_{\text{K}^+}} = \frac{19 - 11.25}{20 - 11.25}; \qquad r_{\text{Ca}^{2+}} = 1.17 \text{ A}, \tag{1-9}$$

and by a similar calculation it is found that the radius of the sulfur ion is 2.19 A. The calculated internuclear distance is $r_{\text{Ca}^{2+}} + r_{\text{S}^{2-}} = 3.36$ A. This result is clearly in error from the measured result.

To remedy this calculation it is necessary to reexamine the model being used to represent an ionic crystal. This model is based on the assumption that ionic crystals are hard spheres held together by electrostatic forces. If, however, we allow the ions to be porous to some degree much like a rubber ball, then the ions become harder as the centers move closer to each other. In more physical terms, we say the ions have a short-range repulsive potential energy in addition to the electrostatic attraction. At the equilibrium distance, the magnitude of the force of attraction is equal to the magnitude of the force of repulsion. To what may this repulsion be attributed? In simple terms it may be answered by noting that as the nuclei of two ions approach each other, the density of electrons between the atoms becomes greater with a consequently larger electrostatic repulsion.

---

* J. C. Slater, *Phys. Rev.* **36,** 57 (1930).

There are many ways to describe the repulsive effect mathematically. Since it arises from the interpenetration of electron clouds, it might be represented, as will be seen in Chapter 3, by an exponential of the form e^{-br}, where r is the internuclear distance. For our convenience in calculation, however, the repulsive potential will be represented by be^2/r^n, where b and n are constants to be determined. For the repulsive force to be operative only at very small distances, n should be a number greater than about 5.

The potential U_i for an ion with a charge of $Z_i e$ in an ionic crystal lattice is the sum of the potential energy terms arising from interaction with each ion of the lattice. It may be written as

$$U_i = \sum_j \left(\frac{-Z_i Z_j e^2}{r_{ij}} + \frac{be^2}{r_{ij}^n} \right). \tag{1-10}$$

The first term is the electrostatic attraction, and the second is the repulsion; r_{ij} is the distance from the ith ion to the jth ion, and the sum does not include $i = j$. Neglecting surface effects, the total lattice energy for $2N$ ions is $U_0 = +NU$. The factor of 2 is necessary to eliminate counting twice interactions between pairs.

Equation (1-10) may be simplified by introducing the nearest neighbor distance, R. Then $r_{ij} = \alpha_{ij} R$, where α_{ij} is a proportionality constant. The potential becomes

$$U_i = \sum_j \left(\frac{-Z_i Z_j e^2}{R \alpha_{ij}} + \frac{be^2}{\alpha_{ij}^n R^n} \right). \tag{1-11}$$

For ionic structures in which $Z_+ e$ is the charge on the cation and $Z_- e$ is the charge on the anion, we may simplify Eq. (1-11) to give, for the potential at a cation,

$$U_i = \frac{-A Z_+ Z_- e^2}{R} + \frac{Be^2}{R^n}, \tag{1-12}$$

where

$$A = \sum_j \frac{Z_j}{Z_-} \alpha_{ij}^{-1}, \qquad B = \sum_j \frac{b}{\alpha_{ij}^n}.$$

A plot of U_i as a function of R is shown in Fig. 1-24. The constant A is called the *Madelung constant* and is a property of the lattice type. It is obtained by summing the inverse distance from an ion to the other ions, with a plus or minus sign being used depending on whether Z_j is Z_+ or Z_-.

Consider the calculation of the Madelung constant for a NaCl lattice, as shown in Fig. 1-20. The potential at a given ion results from

(a) 6 nearest neighbors of opposite charge at a distance R contributing to A +6;

(b) 12 next nearest neighbors of the same charge at a distance $R\sqrt{2}$ contributing $-12/\sqrt{2}$;

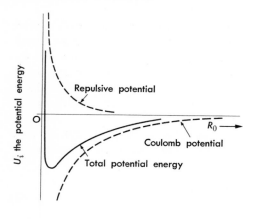

Fig. 1–24. The potential energy as a function of distance between two ions. The total potential energy is the sum of the repulsive and attractive energies.

(c) 8 (next)^2 nearest neighbors of opposite charge at a distance of $R\sqrt{3}$ contributing $+8/\sqrt{3}$;

(d) 6 (next)^3 nearest neighbors of the same charge at a distance of $2R$ contributing -3;

(e) 24 (next)^4 nearest neighbors of the opposite charge at a distance of $R\sqrt{5}$ contributing $+24/\sqrt{5}$.

The process is continued to give, for A,

$$A = +6 - 12/\sqrt{2} + 8/\sqrt{3} - 6/2 + 24/\sqrt{5} - 24/\sqrt{6} + \cdots$$
$$= +6 - 8.486 + 4.619 - 3 + 10.733 - 9.800 + \cdots$$

It is clear that the process of calculating A is a slowly converging process if it is converging at all. The value found after many terms is 1.747558.

It is possible to use a method due to Evjen which results in more rapid convergence. In this method groups of charges which are almost neutral are counted. To do this, fractional charges are used if necessary. The physical reason for this scheme is that the contribution to the potential energy from ions in a spherical shell of thickness Δr at a large distance r from the central ion must be very close to zero since there will be nearly the same amount of positive charge as negative charge. Thus most of the contribution to A must come from ions near the central ion. It is inconvenient, however, to use spherical shells because of the difficulty of taking fractional charges. This problem is overcome by using "shells" whose external shape is that of the unit cell. Since the summation over all the ions of a crystal is stopped after an arbitrary accuracy in A is obtained, the actual manner of summation is immaterial.

Neutral groups are artificially constructed for the NaCl structure by considering the charges in cubic cells with the potential to be evaluated at the center. Let us assume that the charges on cube corners are shared between eight cubes; the charges on the edges, between four cubes; and the charges on the walls, between two cubes. We may pick the first cube for NaCl to be the smallest cubic unit cell whose edge is a_0. Referring to Fig. 1-20 there are about each positive ion

(a) 6 negative ions at a distance R of charge $-\frac{1}{2}e$;

(b) 12 positive ions at a distance $\sqrt{2} R$ of charge $+\frac{1}{4}e$;

(c) 8 negative ions at a distance $\sqrt{3} R$ of charge $-\frac{1}{8}e$.

The total charge of this cell is $-1e$, and the value of A is as follows:

$$A = \frac{6}{1}\left(\frac{1}{2}\right) - \frac{12}{\sqrt{2}}\left(\frac{1}{4}\right) + \frac{8}{\sqrt{3}}\left(\frac{1}{8}\right) = 3 - 2.122 + 0.577 = 1.455.$$

If a cell with an edge of $2a_0$ is used, the value of A is found to be 1.75. It is quite obvious that this process is converging rapidly to the accepted value. Table 1-1 gives the values of Madelung constants for a number of lattices.

TABLE 1-1

A TABLE OF MADELUNG CONSTANTS
FOR SOME COMMON LATTICES

Structure	A
NaCl	1.747558
CsCl	1.76267
Zinc blende	1.63806
Wurtzite	1.641
Fluorite	5.03878
Al$_2$O$_3$, corundum	25.0312

At equilibrium, the net force on the central ion is zero, and as a consequence $dU_i/dR = 0$. Performing this derivative of Eq. (1-12) it is found that

$$\frac{dU_i}{dR} = \frac{Ae^2 Z_+ Z_-}{R^2} - \frac{nBe^2}{R^{n+1}} = 0;$$

$$\therefore R_0 = \left(\frac{nB}{AZ_+ Z_-}\right)^{1/(n-1)}; \tag{1-13}$$

This equation shows that the equilibrium distance between ions, R_0, should vary as $(1/Z_+ Z)^{1/(n-1)}$. Assuming that n and B are the same, we may estimate the effect of having a charge of 2 on the ions rather than unity:

$$\frac{R_0^{+2}}{R_0^{+1}} = \left(\frac{1}{4}\right)^{1/(n-1)}.$$

This suggests that the reason the previous calculation for the CaS interatomic distance was in error is that repulsive effects must be estimated. The ions, K$^+$,

Cl^-, Ca^{2+}, and S^{2-}, all have the argon electron configuration. The value of n for argon configuration ions is about 9, as will be shown below, which gives for the equilibrium distance $0.842 \times 3.36 = 2.83$ A. The measured value of 2.84 A agrees very well, a somewhat fortuitous occurrence.

The radii calculated in Eqs. (1–6) through (1–9) which were proportional to the effective nuclear charge are called univalent radii. These are the radii which the multivalent ions would have if they retained their electronic configurations but acted in the coulomb field as univalent ions.

Equation (1–13) also shows that the equilibrium distance is a function of the type of crystal lattice. For instance, if Z_+, Z_-, and n are constant, the ratio of internuclear distances for NaCl to CsCl lattices is given by

$$\frac{R_0^{NaCl}}{R_0^{CsCl}} = \left[\frac{B^{NaCl} A^{CsCl}}{B^{CsCl} A^{NaCl}} \right]^{1/(n-1)}. \tag{1–14}$$

A reasonable approximation is to take the sum for B over just the nearest neighbors because the repulsive force is a short-range type. We find the ratio of $B^{NaCl}/B^{CsCl} = 6/8$ if the value of b does not change from one crystal form to another. For $n = 9$,

$$\frac{R_0^{NaCl}}{R_0^{CsCl}} = 0.965. \tag{1–15}$$

Similar calculations may be made for other lattices which illustrate that if a compound exists in two crystal lattices, the observed ionic radii will vary. In the specific case calculated above, the interionic distance in a NaCl lattice will be about 5% smaller than in a CsCl lattice.

An estimate for the lattice energy of an ionic crystal may be made from Eqs. (1–11) and (1–13). Solving for B, we obtain

$$B = \frac{A Z_+ Z_-}{n} R_0^{(n-1)}. \tag{1–16}$$

Substituting this expression into Eq. (1–11), we find the lattice energy to be

$$U_0 = N U_i = \frac{N A Z_+ Z e^2}{R_0} \left(1 - \frac{1}{n} \right). \tag{1–17}$$

The first term contains known constants for a given crystal and the only unknown parameter is n, the repulsive term exponent. This term may be determined in the following manner.

If a material is subjected to a uniform pressure, the volume will decrease by an amount proportional to the volume and the pressure change. We may write this as

$$dv = -\beta v \, dp, \tag{1–18}$$

where β is the proportionality constant called the compressibility. This expression may be rewritten as

$$\frac{1}{\beta} = -v \frac{dp}{dv}. \tag{1--19}$$

Such a compression requires that work be done on the system which is just the change in potential energy, dU. The work done is also equal to $-p\,dv$. The volume of a lattice cell is proportional to R^3 so that $dv/v = 3\,dR/R$. We find upon substitution:

$$p = -\frac{R}{3v} \frac{dU}{dR}. \tag{1--20}$$

Substituting Eq. (1--13), we have

$$p = -\frac{1}{3v} \left(\frac{Ae^2 Z_+ Z_-}{R} - \frac{nBe^2}{R^n} \right); \tag{1--21}$$

$$\therefore \frac{1}{\beta} = \frac{1}{9v} \left(-\frac{Ae^2 Z_+ Z_-}{R} + \frac{n^2 Be^2}{R^n} \right) + p. \tag{1--22}$$

If we approximate that at $p = 0$, $R = R_0$, then after substituting Eq. (1--13) we have

$$\frac{1}{\beta} = \frac{Ae^2 Z_+ Z_-}{9V_0 R_0} (n - 1). \tag{1--23}$$

Thus measurements of the compressibility of crystals provide a means to obtain n if the crystal spacing parameters are known. Table 1--2 lists some representative values. Since the dependence of U on n is not important except at very small distances, the accuracy of n is relatively unimportant.

The direct measurement of the crystal energy which is the energy required to form a gas of cations and anions from a crystal is difficult and not very reliable. However, a combination of ionization energies and energies of formation in a process which is known as the Born-Haber cycle may be used to obtain a so-called "experimental" lattice energy.

TABLE 1--2

VALUES OF THE BORN EXPONENT FOR VARIOUS ION TYPES

Ion type	n
He	5
Ne	7
Ar	9
Kr	10
Xe	12

Table 1--3 is a comparison of the theoretical and experimental lattice energies for a number of alkali halides. The agreement is striking. It illustrates that the bulk of the lattice energy of an ionic crystal is the result of coulombic interaction. Many people have refined the calculations to include van der Waals forces and more complex overlap considerations. Such calculations amount to only a few percent of the total energy.

TABLE 1–3

A COMPARISON OF CALCULATED AND
EXPERIMENTAL LATTICE ENERGIES

Crystal	Lattice energy	
	kcal/mole, calculated	kcal/mole, experimental
LiCl	189	201.5
LiBr	189	191.5
LiI	167	180.0
NaCl	178	184.7
NaBr	169	175.9
KCl	164	167.8
KI	148	152.8
RbBr	152	158.0
RbI	147	149.7

The lattice energies will also be affected by several other factors. In the section on packing of spheres, a discussion was presented on the size of spheres that could be placed in the interstitial positions of various lattice arrangements. For ionic crystals this effect is apparent in the observed melting points of solid alkali halides. These data are given in Fig. 1–25. If anion-anion contact is possible, additional electrostatic repulsive forces occur which will lower the lattice energy and, therefore, the melting point. For the NaCl lattice, the critical radius ratio for anion-anion contact is 0.414 because the anions form a face-centered cubic lattice. For all lithium salts, except for LiF, the radius ratio is less than 0.414 so that the melting points are lowered considerably from the predicted values.

Figure 1–25 also shows that LiF and NaI have lower melting points than expected by extrapolation of a smooth curve through the higher molecular weight alkali halides. Therefore, even though the radius ratio is greater than 0.414,

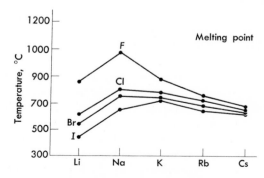

Fig. 1–25. The melting points of the alkali halides.

repulsion between anions is present. This fact illustrates that the idea of an ionic radius is only a convenience for crude calculations but cannot be used to give accurate information about intrinsic properties of matter. Indeed, a quantum-mechanical calculation shows that for all ions, there is a probability of a certain radius which is a function of the state of the ion and the distance from the nucleus. Thus, the concept of a hard or even semihard sphere is a gross approximation to the actual ion. In Chapter 2 another technique will be discussed which measures directly the amount of overlap and effective radius of an ion.

COVALENT CRYSTALS

We have treated two types of crystal lattices, one which involves only short-range spherical forces and the other which involves long-range spherical forces. A third large class of crystals has long-range *directed* forces predominantly responsible for the binding. An example of such a crystal is the diamond lattice. The bonding is called covalent bonding because it arises from the sharing of a pair of electrons between atoms. The directed nature of the covalent bond results from the restricted orbits in which the electrons move. As a consequence of directed bonding, covalent crystal structures tend to be more open than ionic structures. For example, in the diamond lattice, the fraction of space occupied by the atoms is 0.34. Thus, the primary consideration for the type of structure obtained is not packing of spheres but the directional properties of the bond.

Covalent crystals are also characterized by hardness. Diamond is the hardest of all materials. Boron and nitrogen which are on either side of carbon in the periodic table form a compound BN which has the same structure as diamond and is almost as hard. Hardness in noncubic crystals is often a directional property. For instance, kyanite, which is an aluminum silicate, may be scratched with steel along the prism axis but is too hard to scratch in a direction perpendicular to the axis. Again, this is an indication of the directional properties of the covalent bond.

EXAMPLES OF COVALENT LATTICES

One of the most familiar of all covalent lattices is the zinc blende lattice shown in Fig. 1–26. This structure is identical to the diamond structure discussed previously. It is formed by all Group IV elements and binary compounds formed from a Group III element and a Group V element or from a Group II element and a Group VI element. An alternative name for the structure is sphalerite after the natural mineral of ZnS.

In sphalerite each atom is bonded to four other atoms in a tetrahedral arrangement. If the tetrahedra are considered as a unit, the sphalerite lattice corresponds to a cubic close-packing of these units. It is possible to repack the units in a hexagonal close-packing arrangement which is shown in Fig. 1–27.

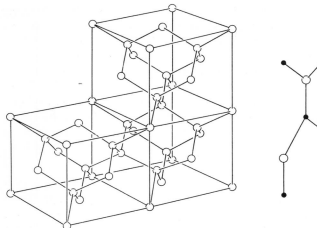

Fig. 1–26. The diamond lattice.

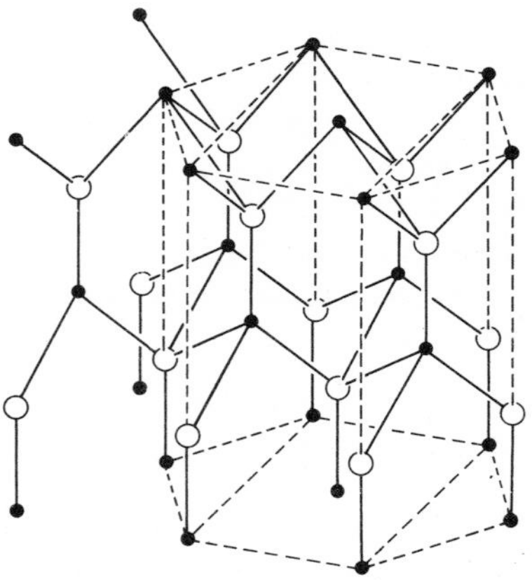

Fig. 1–27. The wurtzite lattice.

The unit cell is hexagonal rather than cubic. The lattice is called the wurtzite lattice and occurs in Group II and VI and Group II and V compounds. Examples are MgTe, CdS, AlN, and BeO.

An interesting point is that some of these crystals may be changed from one form to the other. The Madelung constants are about the same, and one expects that the energy difference is not too large between the two lattices. The classical example is the transition of cubic ZnS to hexagonal ZnS at a temperature of 1040°C. On the other hand, the transition from cubic to hexagonal for CdS occurs at about room temperature.

In addition to covalent structures in three dimensions, there are materials which have essentially one- and two-dimensional lattices. The one-dimensional lattices are called chain lattices, and the two-dimensional lattices, layer lattices. Examples of these are shown in Fig. 1–28. The forces between the layers or chains may be ionic, but in most cases, are weak van der Waals forces. The layer lattice is familiar in the form of graphite, but other examples are $CrCl_3$

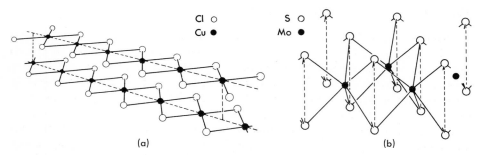

Fig. 1–28. (a) The chain lattice of cupric chloride. (b) The layer lattice of molybdenum disulfide.

and As. The chain lattice is evidenced by $CrCl_2$, $CuCl_2$, and $AlCl_3$. In fact, the first two examples have magnetic properties which can be explained by assuming almost independent chains.

COVALENT RADII

For a homonuclear lattice such as diamond, the obvious method of obtaining the radius of carbon atom is to take one-half the bond distance of 1.54 A. There are, however, only a limited number of examples where this procedure may be used. If the bond distance of a crystal of SiC is measured, it is found to be the sum of the covalent radii obtained from diamond and silicon crystals. This fact suggests that covalent radii are simply additive, provided the bonding is a single electron pair bond between atoms. Examination of a number of diverse compounds including organic molecules such as ethane and ethanol give a consistent C—C bond distance of 1.54 A, which shows that the bond distance is quite independent of the nature of other atoms attached to the carbon atoms. If C—C bond distance of ethene is measured, it is found to be 1.34 A. Since this bond contains two electron pairs, it is reasonable to expect it to be different from the diamond bond distance.

The covalent radii of many atoms may be obtained from the diatomic molecules formed from the elements such as H_2, F_2, Cl_2, Br_2, and I_2. Once again, it is found that radii are closely additive. Table 1–4 is a list of single-bond covalent radii for a number of elements. Some caution must be used because as a bond becomes more ionic, the additivity of these radii decreases. Atoms involved in double or triple bonds will have approximately 10 and 20% smaller radii.

MOLECULAR CRYSTALS

If a crystal is formed of molecules in which only van der Waals forces hold the lattice together, the lattice is called a molecular crystal. As a consequence, the molecules remain nearly the same as in the liquid or gas phases and have relatively small interactions with their neighbors. Examples of molecular crystals are solid benzene, anthracene, and chlorine. The structure of chlorine shows that the distance between chlorine atoms in a molecule is 2.02 A, whereas the closest intermolecular chlorine—chlorine distance is 3.34 A. Obviously, the molecule of Cl_2 is little changed from the gaseous interatomic distance of 2.01 A.

The physical properties of molecular crystals reflect the weak bonding. They are usually soft and deformable. The melting points are low in comparison with ionic crystals, and electrical conduction does not exist.

In concluding this chapter, a comment upon the classification of crystals by means of the type of bonding is needed. There are few crystals which show only a single type of bonding. In general, the bonding between atoms is a mixture as can be demonstrated by consideration of a crystal of CdI_2. The struc-

TABLE 1–4

SINGLE-BOND COVALENT RADII OF THE ELEMENTS

Element	Covalent radius, A	Element	Covalent radius, A
Aluminum	1.25	Manganese	1.17
Antimony	1.41	Mercury	1.44
Argon	1.91	Molybdenum	1.29
Arsenic	1.21	Neon	1.60
Barium	1.98	Nickel	1.15
Beryllium	0.89	Niobium	1.34
Bismuth	1.52	Nitrogen	0.74
Boron	0.80	Oxygen	0.74
Bromine	1.14	Phosphorus	1.10
Cadmium	1.41	Platinum	1.26
Calcium	1.74	Potassium	2.03
Carbon	0.77	Rubidium	2.16
Cerium	1.65	Selenium	1.17
Cesium	2.35	Silicon	1.17
Chlorine	0.99	Silver	1.34
Chromium	1.17	Sodium	1.57
Cobalt	1.16	Strontium	1.91
Copper	1.17	Sulfur	1.04
Fluorine	0.72	Tantalum	1.34
Germanium	1.22	Tellurium	1.37
Gold	1.34	Tin	1.40
Hydrogen	0.28	Titanium	1.32
Iodine	1.33	Tungsten	1.30
Iron	1.17	Uranium	1.42
Lead	1.54	Vanadium	1.22
Lithium	1.23	Zinc	1.25
Magnesium	1.36	Zirconium	1.45

ture is a chain lattice in which the bonds along the chains are partly ionic and partly covalent. The force between chains arises essentially from van der Waals bonding. Therefore, it should always be borne in mind that classification of crystals by bond types is little more than a convenient but qualitative approximation.

REFERENCES

HARVEY, K. B., and G. B. PORTER, *Introduction to Physical Inorganic Chemistry*, Addison-Wesley, Reading, Mass., 1963.

PAULING, L., *The Nature of the Chemical Bond*, Cornell, Ithaca, N. Y., 1960.

WELLS, A. F., *Structural Inorganic Chemistry*, Oxford Press, New York, 1961.

WELLS, A. F., *The Third Dimension in Chemistry*, Butterworth, London, 1956.

PROBLEMS

1. Draw a body-centered cubic lattice. Outline the trigonal cell for this lattice. What are the relative volumes of these two cells?

2. List all the elements of the tetrahedral group. Note that a tetrahedron may be placed in a cube so that the edges of the tetrahedron form face diagonals of the cube, as shown in Fig. 1–19.

3. Show that z, x, y are a degenerate set of symmetry functions of the tetrahedral group.

4. Show that $(3z^2 - 1)$ and $(x^2 - y^2)$ are transformed into each other or a linear combination of each other by the symmetry operation of the cubic group. What other functions which are second degree in x, y, and z transform among themselves? Assume that $x^2 + y^2 + z^2 = 1$.

5. Show that the c/a ratio for hcp is 1.633; c is the length of the 6-fold axis of the unit cell and a is the length of one of the base vectors.

6. Show that the percentage of space filled for a bcc lattice and a fcc lattice of spheres with radius a is 68% and 74%, respectively.

7. Calculate the fraction of the crystal volume occupied by spheres arranged in a diamond lattice and simple cubic lattice. Compare with the fcc and bcc lattices.

8. Construct the Wigner-Seitz cell of the face-centered cubic lattice. What is the volume of this cell relative to the volume of the smallest unit cell with maximum symmetry?

9. Show that the Wigner-Seitz cell obtained in Problem 1–8 has all the symmetry properties of a cube.

10. Calculate the maximum radius ratio r_A/r_B for an atom A to fit in the interstitial positions of a simple cubic B lattice.

11. Consider a NaCl crystal in which the potential energy is reduced by a medium whose dielectric constant is 80. Calculate the lattice energy assuming that the lattice constant is the same as normal sodium chloride. Compare the lattice energy per ion with the thermal energy kT, where $T = 300°K$ and k is the Boltzmann constant.

12. Calculate the Madelung constant for the ZnS and CaF_2 lattices using the Evjen method and two cubes, one with an edge R_0 and the other with an edge $3R_0$.

13. Using the data of Table 1–4, plot the covalent radii as a function of atomic number. What conclusions can you draw from this graph? Note particularly the covalent radius effects along a particular row and column of the periodic table. Compare the ionic and covalent radii of the halogens.

14. Show that the crystal system with $\alpha_1 = \pi/2 \neq \beta \neq \gamma$, and $a_1 \neq a_2 \neq a_3$ belongs to the triclinic system.

15. By direct summation of the series show that for a one-dimensional crystal consisting of alternating charged particles separated by a distance a the Madelung constant is 2 ln 2. Using two cells and the Evjen Method, what numerical value is obtained?

2

X-ray Structural Determination

THE REQUIREMENTS FOR STRUCTURAL DETERMINATION

In the previous chapter it was assumed that the distance between atoms in crystals is approximately two or three angstroms. To "see" these small distances, radiation must be used which has an even smaller wavelength. This is a consequence of the interference patterns set up by the scattered light. It is usually shown in an elementary physics course that the intensity distribution of light perpendicular to a beam as it passes through an aperture is as prescribed in Fig. 2-1. This pattern is known as a Fraunhofer diffraction pattern. The width of the central peak is proportional to the wavelength and inversely proportional to the diameter of the aperture. If one tries to measure the distance between two sources, the separation must be larger than the half width of the interference pattern, otherwise the two patterns will overlap and appear as one source. Figure 2-2 illustrates the diffraction images for resolved and unresolved sources. For optical microscopes using visible light, it may be shown that the limit of resolution is about 2×10^{-5} cm. Consequently, to resolve interatomic spacings, the wavelength must be reduced by a factor of 1000. Fortunately there are several different methods to produce short-wavelength radiation.

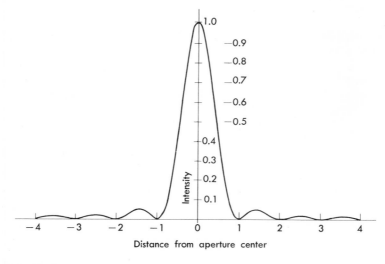

Fig. 2-1. The intensity distribution of a monochromatic beam of light which has passed through a small aperture.

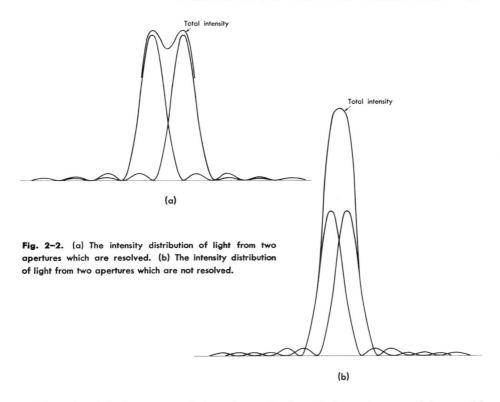

Total intensity

(a)

Total intensity

Fig. 2–2. (a) The intensity distribution of light from two apertures which are resolved. (b) The intensity distribution of light from two apertures which are not resolved.

(b)

First, it might be supposed that the scattering of elementary particles would give structural information. The wavelength of a particle of mass m moving with a velocity v is given by the deBroglie relation, $\lambda = h/mv$, where h is Planck's constant. Using the kinetic energy relationship, $E = \frac{1}{2}mv^2$, it is found that

$$E = \frac{h^2}{2m\lambda^2}.$$
(2–1)

For neutrons the rest mass is one atomic mass unit, which is 1.66×10^{-24} gm. The energy necessary for $\lambda = 10^{-8}$ cm is, therefore, 1.3×10^{-13} ergs, which is approximately that for a particle with energy kT at room temperature. Such neutrons are called thermal neutrons.

The neutron has no charge, and therefore the only interaction of a neutron with matter is that resulting from magnetic interaction of the neutron magnetic dipole with the magnetic properties of the lattice. Neutron diffraction studies are generally useful for studying materials which have large magnetic effects. For example, detailed information about the alignment of the magnetic moments of the ions in crystals such as MnO and $BaTiO_3$ have been obtained. However, the theoretical analyses of the data are more complicated than the corresponding x-ray experiment. In addition, the experiment itself requires an elaborate apparatus to produce and measure monoenergetic and therefore

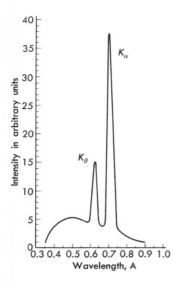

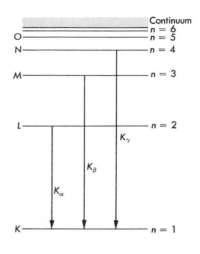

Fig. 2–4. A target-atom energy-level diagram which shows schematically the transitions for K_α, K_β, and K_γ radiation.

Fig. 2–3. The intensity distribution as a function of wavelength for the x-ray spectrum of molybdenum.

monochromatic neutrons. Because of the complexity we will not discuss this technique further.

Another particle which may be used is the electron. Since it has a smaller mass, the energy must be larger than that calculated for the neutron by a factor of about 2000. Thus, electrons must be accelerated through a potential difference of a few hundred volts. Unfortunately, the electron is charged and the penetration of the electron beam is limited to the surface volume of the crystal. Since the information so obtained is more easily procured from x-ray studies, we will not consider electron diffraction.

The third possibility is to use a radiation called *x-radiation* which is produced by striking a metal target with electrons whose energy is approximately 30,000 ev. Collisions of the incident electrons with core electrons of the metal atoms cause radiation, which results from the reshuffling of the metal electrons. A typical spectrum from a molybdenum target is shown in Fig. 2–3.

There are two distinct features of an x-ray emission: (1) a continuous spectrum, and (2) a line spectrum. The continuous spectrum arises from the radiation produced by the incoming electron. The process is much like a reverse photoelectric effect. The minimum wavelength observed corresponds to the maximum energy of the accelerated electrons. Because there is a spread of energies of the electron beam, a broad continuum is obtained.

The line spectrum results from a different process. When an electron with sufficient energy hits a target, there is the possibility that an inner core electron will be kicked out of its orbit. An electron in a higher energy level can lose energy by radiation and go into the vacant energy level. The energy emitted will be characteristic of the energy level diagram of the target atom. The K_α-line in Fig. 2–3 corresponds in energy to the energy difference between the K-shell (principal quantum number, $n = 1$) and the L-shell ($n = 2$). The K_β-line results from a transition from the M-shell ($n = 3$) to the K-shell. Figure 2–4 schematically represents a target-atom energy-level diagram. Some transitions such as the N-to-K transition are not observed in Fig. 2–3 because the initial energy of the electron beam is insufficient.

For the K_α-line the experimental results closely fit the expression

$$\nu_{K_\alpha} = \tfrac{3}{4}R(Z - 1)^2, \qquad (2\text{–}2)$$

where R is a constant, ν is the frequency of the radiation, and Z is the atomic number of the metal. As the atomic number is increased, the wavelength of the radiation decreases. This result was discovered by Moseley prior to World War I and was instrumental in establishing the order of the periodic table by atomic number rather than atomic weight.

THE INTERACTION OF X–RAYS WITH MATTER

We might expect that x-rays are absorbed by materials just as ordinary visible light is. Some materials should be "transparent" and others should have stronger absorption. For elements with low atomic numbers, the density of electrons is small. Since absorption of energy must be done by electrons, these materials will be poor absorbers. Similarly, we may expect that the "heavier" elements will exhibit stronger absorption because the electron density is larger.

When absorption occurs, it is found that the decrease in intensity per unit length is proportional to the intensity and the density ρ of the material. We may express this mathematically as

$$-\frac{dI}{dl} = \mu\rho I, \qquad (2\text{–}3)$$

where μ is a proportionality constant characteristic of the material and is called the *absorption coefficient*. Equation (2–3) may be integrated to give

$$I = I_0 e^{-\mu\rho l}, \qquad (2\text{–}4)$$

where I_0 is the incident intensity of the beam and I is the emergent intensity. When the energy of an x-ray is sufficient to kick an electron from an inner shell, the absorption coefficient for that wavelength increases sharply and the absorption can be used as a filter for x-rays. It is possible to reduce the K_β-radiation by a factor of $\frac{1}{600}$ for x-rays from a cobalt target by using an iron filter, because the K_β-frequency almost matches an iron transition. The K_α-radiation, on the other hand, is reduced by a factor of only 2 or 3. Therefore, a source of monochromatic radiation is available with known wavelength.

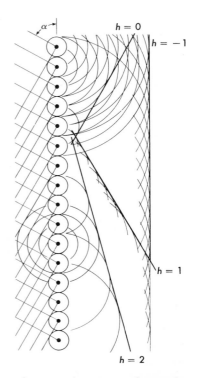

Fig. 2–5. The scattering of a plane wave by a one-dimensional lattice. Each lattice point emits a spherical wave with the maximum amplitude represented by the circular lines. Points of intersection are points of maximum amplitude of the scattered waves.

X-rays are not only absorbed and dissipated into heat but can also be scattered by electrons. Qualitatively, we can see that if an electron is accelerated and decelerated by an oscillating electric field, it will emit energy in the form of radiation with the same frequency as the electric field. The scattered radiation is emitted as spherical waves. In the case we are considering, the x-ray is actually an oscillating electromagnetic field.

The electrons of the atoms scatter the x-radiation in spherical waves, which are represented in Fig. 2–5 by circles indicating a constant amplitude called wave fronts. It is seen that a wave front is formed whenever scattered waves from the row reinforce the amplitude. Several such wave fronts are drawn in Fig. 2–5. The wave formed parallel to the incident wave is the zeroth-order wave front. The wave front with the smallest angle with respect to the zeroth-order front is the first-order front, etc.

To derive an expression for the angle of the scattered wave as a function of the incident wave angle, consider Fig. 2–6, which more clearly illustrates the geometry. The incident wave front AB is scattered by atoms x and y. To obtain a reinforced wave front at XD, the path difference $\overline{YD} - \overline{CX}$ must be an integral multiple h of the wavelength. That is,

$$\overline{YD} - \overline{CX} = h\lambda. \tag{2–5}$$

Now $\cos \alpha = \overline{CX}/d$ and $\cos \beta = \overline{YD}/d$, where d is the distance between scattering centers. Substituting into Eq. (2–5) we find

$$d(\cos \beta - \cos \alpha) = h\lambda. \tag{2–6}$$

For the special case of $\alpha = \pi/2$, $h\lambda/d = \cos \beta$. The scattered radiation forms cones with the row of atoms as the axes. The values of h correspond to the zeroth-, first-, second-, etc., order wave fronts. Similar equations may be obtained by considering plane lattices and three-dimensional lattices. Equations such as Eq. (2–6) are known as the Laue equations of diffraction.

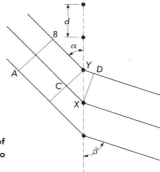

Fig. 2–6. A schematic drawing of wave front being scattered by two lattice points.

If the angles of incidence and reflection are measured with respect to a perpendicular to the row of atoms, then Eq. (2–6) becomes

$$h\lambda = d(\sin \alpha - \sin \beta). \qquad (2\text{--}7)$$

In addition, if the experiment is arranged so that $\alpha = -\beta$, that is, the source and detector are varied simultaneously, scattering is observed at

$$h\lambda = 2d \sin \alpha, \qquad (2\text{--}8)$$

or defining $d_h = d/h$, we have

$$\lambda = 2d_h \sin \alpha. \qquad (2\text{--}9)$$

For two dimensions, the ideas given above may be expanded in a logical fashion. Since each plane is specified by two numbers, the parameter d has two indices, and the wavelength is

$$\lambda = 2d_{hk} \sin \alpha_{hk}, \qquad (2\text{--}10)$$

where for an orthogonal lattice with lattice spacings of a and b,

$$d_{hk} = \left[\left(\frac{h}{a}\right)^2 + \left(\frac{k}{b}\right)^2 \right]^{-1/2}. \qquad (2\text{--}11)$$

For a three-dimensional orthogonal lattice, the equation is analogous:

$$\lambda = 2d_{hkl} \sin \alpha_{hkl}, \qquad (2\text{--}12)$$

$$d_{hkl} = [(h/a)^2 + (k/b)^2 + (l/c)^2]^{-1/2}. \qquad (2\text{--}13)$$

Equations (2–9), (2–10), and (2–12) are known as the Bragg diffraction equations.

One of the common methods of obtaining an x-ray pattern is to orient a crystal so that it rotates about a symmetry axis. The incident x-rays are collimated into a beam which is perpendicular to the axis of rotation. The film which is used as a detector is rolled into a cylinder so that the axis of the cylinder is the axis of rotation of the crystal. A typical arrangement is shown in Fig. 2–7. The theoretical analysis is similar to that given for scattering by a row of atoms as discussed above with the exception that the diffracted beams now lie along the intersections of cones. The reason for this may be seen as follows: In a three-dimensional array of atoms, there are rows of atoms not only collinear with the axis of rotation but also at definite angles with respect to the rotation axis depending upon the crystal structure. Each of these rows must diffract x-rays according to the Laue

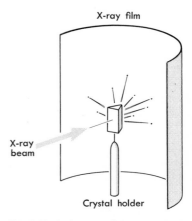

Fig. 2–7. A drawing of the experimental apparatus for taking a rotating crystal photograph.

equations. However, in order to satisfy the requirement that the scattered waves constructively interfere for all rows, the scattered radiation must lie along only the lines of intersection of cones. A photograph of the scattered radiation will appear as spots scattered regularly on the film. The pattern obtained for a crystal of iron cupferron is shown in Fig. 2–8. The photograph is characterized by rows of dots which are caused by exposure of the film to the diffracted x-ray beam. The primary beam is absorbed by a post whose shadow is seen in the figure. The row of spots along the midline of the picture is the zeroth row. The first layer consists of those spots on either side of the zeroth row, etc.

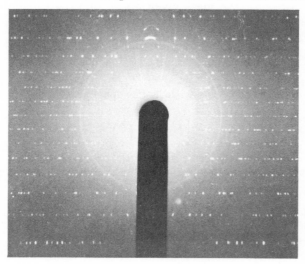

Fig. 2–8. An x-ray photograph of iron cupferron showing the layer lines. This photograph was made by crystal oscillation instead of full rotation.

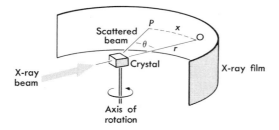

Fig. 2–9. A drawing of the rotating crystal apparatus. The point P is a spot on the film. The unscattered x-ray hits the film at point O. The distance from the film to the crystal is r and the angle of scattering is θ.

The spots on the zeroth layer are related to the lattice spacings as can be seen from Fig. 2–9. Let us consider the rotation axis as the z-axis. Then the angle θ is given by

$$\theta = 2\alpha = \frac{x}{r}\,\text{rad}; \tag{2–14}$$

$$\therefore d_{hk0} = \frac{\lambda}{2 \sin{(x/2r)}}. \tag{2–15}$$

The indices for a rotation about the z-axis are $(hk0)$ for the zeroth layer, $(hk1)$ for the first layer, etc. From the distance between layers the interplanar spacing along the z-axis may be obtained. If the distance from the zeroth layer to the first layer is A, then the lattice spacing d_{001} is

$$d_{001} = \frac{(A^2 + r^2)^{1/2}}{A}. \tag{2–16}$$

A rotating crystal photograph cannot be indexed in an unambiguous manner. In three-dimensional space, three coordinates are needed to specify a plane. As shown previously, these coordinates are related to h, k, and l. Measurements on a rotating crystal photograph give only two coordinates with the result that spots can be indexed partially. For example, if a cubic crystal is rotated about a principal axis, the spots in any layer line are indexed by h and k but are determined by Eq. (2–12). The only restriction for the zeroth layer is that

$$d_{hk0} = a(h^2 + k^2)^{-1/2},$$

where a is the lattice constant.

To overcome the ambiguity of the indexing, a third film coordinate is introduced by moving the camera while rotating the crystal. If this is done in a synchronous manner, each spot will be indexed by three measurements, and therefore can be indexed with an unambiguous set of (hkl). One such technique is called the Weissenberg method.

INTENSITY MEASUREMENTS

Up to the present, we have omitted discussion of one additional variable which can be measured; that is, the intensity of the scattered x-ray beam. This measurement may be performed directly with a specialized scintillation detector or by measuring the optical density of the spots on a photographic plate caused by the x-rays.

To interpret the intensity pattern we must examine the nature of x-rays in more detail than the geometrical treatment we have been using. X-rays are a high-energy form of radiation which must be describable by a set of differential equations governing all electromagnetic phenomena. These equations were first postulated by James Clerk Maxwell prior to the twentieth century. It is not within the purpose of this book to examine these equations in detail, and consequently we will only give a result of combining them. For all radiation the electric and magnetic field vectors $\mathbf{E}$ and $\mathbf{H}$ which describe the radiation obey the equations

$$\nabla^2\mathbf{E} = \frac{1}{c^2}\frac{\partial^2\mathbf{E}}{\partial t^2}, \tag{2-17}$$

$$\nabla^2\mathbf{H} = \frac{1}{c^2}\frac{\partial^2\mathbf{H}}{\partial t^2}, \tag{2-18}$$

where the quantity ∇^2 in cartesian coordinates is

$$\nabla^2 = \frac{\partial^2}{\partial x^2} + \frac{\partial^2}{\partial y^2} + \frac{\partial^2}{\partial z^2}. \tag{2-19}$$

Since Eqs. (2–17) and (2–18) have the same form, we may focus our attention on that describing the $\mathbf{E}$-vector. If we assume that $\mathbf{E} = E(x, t)$, then we have a simpler equation which will illustrate the nature of Eq. (2–17):

$$\frac{\partial^2 E}{\partial x^2} = \frac{1}{c^2}\frac{\partial^2 E}{\partial t^2}. \tag{2-20}$$

The term on the right, $\partial^2 E/\partial t^2$, is much like an acceleration, but it is an electric field instead of a distance derivative. The left-hand side of Eq. (2–20) is the rate of change of slope of the electric field. We might say that the left-hand side is the "lumpiness" of the electric field, because if it were zero, the slope of E would be constant. Equation (2–20) physically expresses the knowledge that the "lumpiness" is proportional to the acceleration of the electric vector. The proportionality constant is just the reciprocal of the square of the velocity of light.

Let us seek a solution of Eq. (2–20) in order to clarify the physical meaning. If we let $E(x, t) = A(x)B(t)$, that is, just the product of functions of single variables, we find that Eq. (2–20) becomes two equations in one variable each:

$$\frac{\partial^2}{\partial x^2}[A(x)B(t)] = \frac{1}{c^2}\frac{\partial^2}{\partial t^2}[A(x)B(t)],$$

which becomes

$$B(t)\frac{\partial^2 A(x)}{\partial x^2} = \frac{1}{c^2}A(x)\frac{\partial^2 B(t)}{\partial t^2},$$

or rewriting, we have

$$\frac{c^2}{A(x)}\frac{\partial^2 A(x)}{\partial x^2} = \frac{1}{B(t)}\frac{\partial^2 B(t)}{\partial t^2}. \qquad (2\text{--}21)$$

The left-hand side of Eq. (2–21) is a function of x only, whereas the right-hand side is a function of t only. Therefore, each must be a constant, say $-\omega^2$:

$$\frac{1}{B(t)}\frac{\partial^2 B(t)}{\partial t^2} = -\omega^2, \qquad \frac{c^2}{A(x)}\frac{\partial^2 A(x)}{\partial t^2} = -\omega^2. \qquad (2\text{--}22)$$

These equations are easily integrated to give

$$B(t) = B_0 e^{i\omega t}, \qquad \text{and} \qquad A(x) = A_0 e^{i\omega x/c}, \qquad (2\text{--}23)$$

which, when multiplied together, give the desired solution:

$$E(x, t) = E_0 e^{i\omega(t+x/c)}. \qquad (2\text{--}24)$$

If we use the Euler equation, $e^{i\phi} = \cos\phi + i\sin\phi$, we may reexpress Eq. (2–24) in the form

$$E(x, t) = E_0[\cos\omega(t + x/c) + i\sin\omega(t + x/c)]. \qquad (2\text{--}25)$$

A plot of the real part of $E(x, t)$ is shown in Fig. 2–10 as a function of t for various values of x/c. The obtained graph shows clearly the reason for consider-

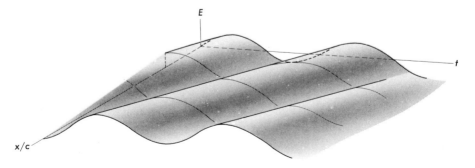

Fig. 2–10. A plot of an electric field as a function of time for various phase angles. The wave-like motion is readily apparent.

ing x-rays as waves. The frequency is just the constant ω, and $\omega x/c$ is called the phase shift of the wave. We may now reexamine the physical meaning of Eq. (2–20) by using Fig. 2–10. The wave is a distribution of electric fields which moves through a medium with velocity c. The electric field at a given point in the medium changes with a "velocity" $\partial E/\partial t$ which is determined by the shape of the wave as it passes.

We can also plot Eq. (2–25) in the complex plane with the real part as the abscissa and the imaginary part as the ordinate. This plot, as shown in Fig. 2–11, is just a circle of radius E_0. The effect of $e^{i\omega t}$ is to rotate E_0 in the complex plane from a position along the real axis if x/c is zero. Similarly $e^{i\omega x/c}$ rotates the initial starting angle for E_0 through an angle $\omega x/c$ rad.

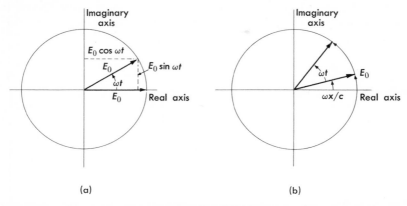

Fig. 2–11. A plot is the complex plane of Eq. (2–25). (a) The phase angle is zero. As t varies, E_0 describes a circle. (b) The phase angle is $(\omega x/c)$, which changes the starting point of E_0 from the real axis by rotation through the angle $\omega x/c$.

To relate the intensity of the x-ray to the electric vector, we may note that at a given instant of time, the power associated with the electric field is proportional to E^2.* The time average may be easily found by integrating over one cycle. Since power is the rate of transfer of energy, it is identical to the intensity of the beam.

In seeking a solution to Eq. (2–20) we picked only one possible solution. We also could have found that

$$E_i = E_{0i}e^{i(\omega_i t + \phi_i)}, \tag{2–26}$$

where $\phi_i = \omega_i x_i/c$, is a solution or indeed any sum of such equations is a solution. That is,

$$E = E_{01}e^{i(\omega_1 t + \phi_1)} + E_{02}e^{i(\omega_2 t + \phi_2)} + \cdots = \sum_{n=1}^{\infty} E_{0n}e^{i(\omega_n t + \phi_n)}. \tag{2–27}$$

---

* The student may recall from Ohm's law that the power is E^2/R for a constant load resistance R.

The typical x-ray diffraction experiment involves the analysis of the synthesized waves which result from the scattering of the incident wave. The scattered wave must have the form of Eq. (2–27). However, the generality of Eq. (2–27) is greatly reduced by the condition of the experiment. The restrictions are:

(a) The x-ray beam is reasonably monochromatic; therefore, ω is a constant.

(b) The spacings of the atoms restrict the number of phase possibilities.

(c) The value of E_n which depends on the incident intensity also depends on the ability of a given atom to scatter x-rays. This intrinsic property is called the atomic scattering power and is denoted by f_i.

Let us reexamine the one-dimensional lattice of Fig. 2–5 in which all atoms were evenly spaced and of the same type. If we let E_0 be unit intensity, the scattered waves have the form

$$E = fe^{i\omega t} \sum_{m=1}^{n} e^{i\phi_m}. \tag{2–28}$$

To perform this summation, let us suppose that the phase of the scattered wave of atom 1 is ϕ and that each atom shifts the phase by a constant angle χ. Then the phase of the wave from atom 2 is $\phi + \chi$; from atom 3, $\phi + 2\chi$; from atom n, $\phi + (n-1)\chi$. Equation (2–28) may be rewritten to give

$$E = fe^{i(\omega t+\phi)} \sum_{m=0}^{n-1} e^{im\chi}. \tag{2–29}$$

The summation $\sum_{m=0}^{n-1} e^{im\chi}$ is a geometric series of the form

$$1 + r + r^2 + \cdots + r^m = S_{m+1}, \quad \text{with} \quad r = e^{i\chi}. \tag{2–30}$$

If Eq. (2–30) is multiplied by r and the result is subtracted from (2–30), we find

$$S_{m+1} - rS_{m+1} = 1 - r^{m+1} \quad \text{or} \quad S_{m+1} = \frac{1 - r^{m+1}}{1 - r}.$$

Therefore,

$$S_n = \frac{1 - e^{in\chi}}{1 - e^{i\chi}} = e^{i(n-1)\chi/2} \frac{\sin (n/2)\chi}{\sin \chi/2}. \tag{2–31}$$

Examination of this equation shows that for $\chi = 2\pi h$, where h is an integer, S_n is 0/0. By invoking L'Hospital's rule for indeterminants, we find

$$S_n(\chi = 2\pi h) = n,$$

or

$$\frac{\sin (n/2)\chi}{n \sin \chi/2} = 1 \quad \text{for} \quad \chi = 2\pi h. \tag{2–32}$$

At other values of χ, (S_n/n) is very small for n large. Thus the only phase angles at which appreciable intensity is observed are those for $h = 0, \pm 1, \pm 2 \ldots$, which correspond to the orders of diffraction we obtained geometrically.

Now let us consider a one-dimensional crystal in which all atoms are not the same, but which has a unit cell. Such a crystal is shown in Fig. 2–12 in which the cell length is d. Each atom scatters x-rays but with different scattering powers for each type. Again we ask, what are the phase relationships in Eq. (2–27) for such a lattice?

Fig. 2–12. A one-dimensional crystal whose unit cell has a length d. There are four different ions in each unit cell.

The answer may be obtained by artificially separating the lattice into the sum of several lattices consisting of identical atoms spaced a distance d. Each sublattice scatters x-rays as given by Eq. (2–29). We may write the total scattering equation as a sum of equations of the form of Eq. (2–29) in which the scattering power and the phase, ϕ, depend on the atom and its position in the unit cell:

$$E = (f_1 e^{i\phi_1} + f_2 e^{i\phi_2} + f_3 e^{i\phi_3} + \cdots) e^{i\omega t} \frac{\sin n\chi/2}{\sin \chi/2}. \qquad (2\text{--}33)$$

Since the phases of each atom in a cell depend upon its position in the cell, it is possible to express the sum in the parentheses in terms of these known quantities. Let the positions of the atoms in a cell be denoted by x_i, the fractional distance of the unit cell length. For hth-order scattering due to the restriction on χ, the phase change in a unit cell is $2\pi h$ rad. Consequently, the phase change in a fractional distance, x_i, will be $2\pi h x_i$. Therefore, we may write Eq. (2–33) as

$$E = (f_1 e^{i2\pi h x_1} + f_2 e^{i2\pi h x_2} + \cdots f_j e^{i2\pi h x_j}) e^{i\omega t} \frac{\sin n\chi/2}{\sin \chi/2}$$

$$= \sum_g f_g e^{i2\pi h x_g} e^{i\omega t} \frac{\sin n\chi/2}{\sin \chi/2}$$

$$\equiv F_h e^{i\omega t} \frac{\sin n\chi/2}{\sin \chi/2}. \qquad (2\text{--}34)$$

The values of F_h are called the structure factors of the lattice, since the atomic positions are contained in it.

For a three-dimensional lattice, the arguments presented for the one-dimensional lattice may be extended. There will be three indices depending upon the plane causing the scattering, and each atom will be positioned by the components of the unit cell vectors. The resulting equation for the structure factor is

$$F_{hkl} = \sum_g f_g e^{2\pi i(hx_g + ky_g + lz_g)}. \qquad (2\text{--}35)$$

APPLICATION OF SYMMETRY TO STRUCTURE FACTORS

The structure factor for many crystal lattices may be simplified by examining the lattice symmetry As an example of this, consider a lattice with inversion symmetry. Every point (x, y, z) has a corresponding point at $(-x, -y, -z)$. Therefore, the structure factor equation will contain pairs of functions which combine to give

$$e^{2\pi i(hx_j+ky_j+lz_j)} + e^{2\pi i(-hx_j-ky_j-lz_j)} = 2\cos 2\pi(hx_j + ky_j + lz_j). \qquad (2\text{-}36)$$

Consequently, any crystal with a center of symmetry has only real cosine terms in the structure factor equation.

A second example of the effect of symmetry is that afforded by a sodium chloride lattice. Beside the center of symmetry, the ions in the unit cell have the following position coordinates:

$$\text{Na}^+ \quad (0, 0, 0) \quad (0, \tfrac{1}{2}, \tfrac{1}{2}) \quad (\tfrac{1}{2}, 0, \tfrac{1}{2}) \quad (\tfrac{1}{2}, \tfrac{1}{2}, 0),$$
$$\text{Cl}^- \quad (\tfrac{1}{2}, \tfrac{1}{2}, \tfrac{1}{2}) \quad (\tfrac{1}{2}, 0, 0) \quad (0, \tfrac{1}{2}, 0) \quad (0, 0, \tfrac{1}{2}).$$

Let us consider the structure factor contribution for the Na^+ at $(0, 0, 0)$ and the Cl^- at $(\tfrac{1}{2}, \tfrac{1}{2}, \tfrac{1}{2})$. We see that Na^+ contributes a factor of $+2$ for all h, k, l, whereas the Cl^- contributes a factor of ± 2 depending upon whether $h + k + l$ is odd or even. As may be readily shown by examination, the other ion pairs have the same relationship. The structure factor for a NaCl lattice is

$$
\begin{aligned}
F_{hkl} &= 4(f_{\text{Na}} + f_{\text{Cl}}) \qquad \text{if} \quad h + k + l \text{ is even,} \\
&= 4(f_{\text{Na}} - f_{\text{Cl}}) \qquad \text{if} \quad h + k + l \text{ is odd.}
\end{aligned}
\qquad (2\text{-}37)
$$

ELECTRON DENSITY MAPS

After the intensities of the various spots on a photographic film for an unknown structure are measured and indexed, the crystallographer tries to extract from these data values of F_{hkl}. Unfortunately, only the value of $|F_{hkl}|^2$ is obtained from the intensity. This obstacle plagues all crystallographers because the phase must be estimated in structure determination.

From a knowledge of the structure factors, values of the electron density, $\rho(x, y, z)$, at points within the unit cell may be obtained from

$$\rho(x, y, z) = \frac{1}{V} \sum_{hkl} F_{hkl} e^{-2\pi i(hx+ky+lz)} \qquad (2\text{-}38)$$

where V is the volume of the unit cell. To perform the summation of this infinite series even for a finite number of F_{hkl} requires the use of high-speed digital computers in order to calculate a crystal structure in a reasonable period of time.

An electron density map for NaCl is shown in Fig. 2–13. Contour lines of constant electron density clearly distinguish the Na^+ from the Cl^-. The elec-

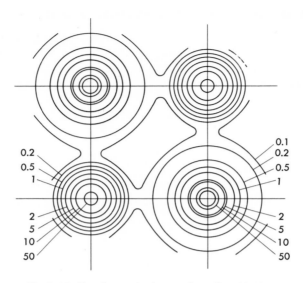

Fig. 2–13. The electron density map for sodium chloride.

tron density between the ions falls to a very small value so that we may define an ionic radius for the Na^+ ion and Cl^- ion as the distance from the center of the ion to the minimum density along the line of centers between cation and anion neighbors. The measured value for Cl^- is 1.64 A and that for Na^+ is 1.17 A. These values may be compared with the ionic radii calculated in Chapter 1 which were 1.81 for Cl^- and 0.95 for Na^+. Using the x-ray values, a set of radii for all ions may be determined. Table 2–1 lists representative values for the alkali metal ions and the halide ions. It should be emphasized that electron density maps which give meaningful densities are difficult to construct. For instance, the sum in Eq. (2–39) is an infinite sum which must be approximated by the finite summation over the observed F_{hkl}. The omitted terms may cause a large deviation in the electron density calculation. Consequently, although they are preferable to the Pauling radii, the values for the radii in Table 2–1

TABLE 2–1

A List of Ionic Radii Obtained from
X-ray Electron Density Maps

Ion	Ionic radius, A	Ion	Ionic radius, A
Na^+	1.17	Cl^-	1.64
K^+	1.49	Br^-	1.80
Rb^+	1.63	I^-	2.05
Cs^+	1.86		

are to be used only as a simplified convenience in discussions involving bond lengths and "sizes." We emphasize once more that the actual radius of an atom can be discussed accurately only in terms of the probability of a certain radius value.

ABSORPTION OF LIGHT OF LONGER WAVELENGTHS

The usefulness of x-rays as a structural probe arises from the fact that lattice distances are approximately the same as the wavelength of an x-ray. Thus, if the wavelength of radiation is increased, the lattice information becomes more diffuse until no information is obtained. However, if the wavelength of the radiation is increased until the energy is approximately that of the binding energies of the electrons involved in bond formation, then absorption and emission of radiation by these electrons occur. It may be expected that measurements of these wavelengths will give detailed information about the binding of atoms in compounds and in effect more detailed knowledge of the immediate surroundings of an atom.

The wavelengths of the radiation spectrum are divided into several arbitrary sections. The region from 1000 A to 4000 A is the ultraviolet region; 4000 A to 6500 A, the visible region; 6500 A to 0.1 cm, the infrared region; 0.1 to 200 cm, the microwave region; and from 200 cm to longer wavelengths, the radio frequency region.

To understand emission and absorption of radiation, recourse must be made to quantum mechanics. Although the intelligent use of quantum mechanics requires a certain mathematical sophistication which is beyond that presumed for the reader, nevertheless, several of the concepts may be used in a pictorial fashion and some calculations may be made without detailed understanding. For a more detailed introduction to quantum mechanics the student is referred to the references at the end of Chapter 3.

REFERENCES

BIJVOET, J. M., N. H. KOLKMEYER, and C. H. MACGILLAVRY, *X-ray Analysis of Crystals*, Butterworths, London, 1951.

BUNN, C. W., *Chemical Crystallography*, Clarendon Press, Oxford, 1961.

BURGER, M. J., *X-ray Crystallography*, John Wiley, New York, 1942.

EVANS, R. C., *Crystal Chemistry*, Cambridge University Press, Cambridge, 1952.

International Tables for X-ray Crystallography, Kynock Press, Birmingham, England, 1962.

PROBLEMS

1. Calculate the structure factor for (a) a CsCl lattice and (b) a sphalerite lattice.

2. From Fig. 2–3, estimate the $L(n = 3$ to $n = 2)$ x-ray wavelength for molybdenum. Check your answer with that given by a handbook of physics.

3. Show that Eq. (2–16) is correct.

4. The powder method of x-ray analysis is carried out simply by replacing the crystal in Fig. 2–7 with a thin-walled glass tube containing the powdered sample. All orientations of the crystal are present in the x-ray beam if the particle size is small enough. (a) Show that cones of scattered radiation result. (b) Draw a diagram of the film pattern expected.

5. Why is it difficult to determine the positions of hydrogen atoms in a structure?

6. The following data were obtained from a single crystal of cadmium sulfide using a rotation camera as in Fig. 2–7. The x-ray tube had a copper target, and a nickel filter was used. The wavelength of the radiation was 1.5418 A. The diameter of the camera was 5.71 cm.

Layer lines	Distance between layers, cm
1, −1	1.44
2, −2	3.00
3, −3	6.00

What axis of the hexagonal crystal was the rotational axis? Use a handbook to obtain the accepted value for the lattice distance.

7. Show that Eq. (2–11) is true for a two-dimensional orthogonal lattice.

8. Calculate the values of $(\sin \alpha/\lambda)$ at which scattering occurs for $(1, 0, 0)$, $(1, 1, 0)$, $(1, 1, 1)$, and $(2, 1, 0)$ planes of NaCl. The density of NaCl is 2.165.

9. Show that for a given wavelength, the relative error in the cell dimension is given by

$$\frac{\Delta d_H}{d_H} = -(\cot \alpha) \, \Delta\alpha.$$

How accurately would one have to measure the angle α to have an error of 0.01 A in the Na—Cl bond distance in a NaCl crystal, assuming that α is $\pi/4$ rad?

3

The Elements of the
Quantum Mechanics of Atoms

THE HYDROGEN ATOM

The simplest of all atomic systems to analyze mathematically is the hydrogen atom, which consists of a single electron interacting with a proton. Since both particles are charged, the major interaction results in a coulombic potential energy of the form

$$V = -e^2/r, \qquad (3\text{-}1)$$

where r is the distance separating the two particles. As mentioned previously, Eq. (3–1) has the symmetry of a sphere under any rotation of the system.

To obtain the total classical energy we must add to Eq. (3–1) the kinetic energy of each particle, which is

$$\text{KE} = \tfrac{1}{2}m_\mathrm{p}(\dot{x}_\mathrm{p}^2 + \dot{y}_\mathrm{p}^2 + \dot{z}_\mathrm{p}^2) + \tfrac{1}{2}m_\mathrm{e}(\dot{x}_\mathrm{e}^2 + \dot{y}_\mathrm{e}^2 + \dot{z}_\mathrm{e}^2), \qquad (3\text{-}2)$$

where $\dot{x}_\mathrm{p}$, $\dot{y}_\mathrm{p}$, and $\dot{z}_\mathrm{p}$ are the velocities of the proton and $\dot{x}_\mathrm{e}$, $\dot{y}_\mathrm{e}$, and $\dot{z}_\mathrm{e}$ are the velocities of the electron in the x-, y-, and z-directions. Because the total energy must be conserved, it is usually convenient to use the energy expression for further calculations.

Since the attractive force acts along a straight line joining the two particles and since there are no external forces, we may separate the total energy into two parts; one is the energy due to the motion of the atom as a whole and the other is energy due to the rotation of the electron and proton about the center of gravity. The coordinates of the center of gravity are

$$X = \frac{m_\mathrm{p}x_\mathrm{p} + m_\mathrm{e}x_\mathrm{e}}{M}, \qquad Y = \frac{m_\mathrm{p}y_\mathrm{p} + m_\mathrm{e}y_\mathrm{e}}{M}, \qquad Z = \frac{m_\mathrm{p}z_\mathrm{p} + m_\mathrm{e}z_\mathrm{e}}{M}, \qquad (3\text{-}3)$$

where $M = m_\mathrm{p} + m_\mathrm{e}$. The corresponding momenta are

$$P_x = M\dot{X}, \qquad P_y = M\dot{Y}, \qquad P_z = M\dot{Z}. \qquad (3\text{-}4)$$

Let us also define:

$$x \equiv x_\mathrm{p} - x_\mathrm{e}, \qquad y \equiv y_\mathrm{p} - y_\mathrm{e}, \qquad \text{and} \qquad z \equiv z_\mathrm{p} - z_\mathrm{e}, \qquad (3\text{-}5)$$

and the momenta,

$$p_x \equiv \mu\dot{x}, \qquad p_y \equiv \mu\dot{y}, \qquad p_z \equiv \mu\dot{z}, \qquad (3\text{-}6)$$

where

$$\frac{1}{\mu} = \frac{1}{m_\mathrm{e}} + \frac{1}{m_\mathrm{p}}.$$

Then by substitution and rearrangement of terms we find that

$$E = \text{KE} + V = \frac{P^2}{2M} + \frac{p^2}{2\mu} - \frac{e^2}{r},\qquad(3\text{-}7)$$

where

$$P^2 = P_x^2 + P_y^2 + P_z^2$$

and

$$p^2 = p_x^2 + p_y^2 + p_z^2.$$

The first term is the energy associated with the translation of the center of mass. The last two terms are the energy which depends on the distance between the particles and the relative velocities and thus is called the *internal* energy. The mass, μ, is referred to as the *reduced* mass. For hydrogen, $m_p \simeq 1800 m_e$ so that $\mu \simeq m_e$.

For large bodies moving with small velocities, Eq. (3–7) is quite accurate, but for small elementary particles the problem becomes more complex. We have referred to the wave nature of elementary particles in Chapter 2. It is this character which invalidates the use of classical mechanics for atomic systems. E. Schroedinger and W. Heisenberg were the first to formulate a wave theory of matter, which has since become known as quantum mechanics or wave mechanics to distinguish it from classical mechanics.

Each system is assumed to be described by a function called the *wave function*. In the simplest terms it is a function of the position coordinates only. To obtain the value of a given property, such as energy, an operator must be found which is associated with the property. By operating on the wave function, a value for the property is obtained. For example, the operator associated with the energy is called the Hamiltonian operator, $\mathcal{H}$. If the wave function is ψ, then

$$\mathcal{H}\psi = E\psi,\qquad(3\text{-}8)$$

where E is the value of energy for the particular wave function. Equation (3–8) is called Schroedinger's equation. We have already dealt with a similar equation in Chapter 2 in the discussion of the wave equation for radiation. Rewriting Eq. (2–22) as

$$\left(\frac{\partial^2}{\partial t^2}\right) B(t) = -\omega^2 B(t),\qquad(3\text{-}9)$$

we see that the operator $\partial^2/\partial t^2$ has the value $-\omega^2$ when operated on the function $B(t)$.

The prescription for obtaining the Hamiltonian operator consists of the following steps:

(1) To write the classical energy expression in terms of position coordinates and momenta.

(2) To replace the momenta by the operators

$$\frac{\hbar}{i}\frac{\partial}{\partial x} \text{ for } p_x, \qquad \frac{\hbar}{i}\frac{\partial}{\partial y} \text{ for } p_y, \qquad \frac{\hbar}{i}\frac{\partial}{\partial z} \text{ for } p_z,$$

where $\hbar$ is Planck's constant divided by 2π.

(3) To make no change in the position coordinates, for they are the operators themselves.

Thus the Hamiltonian for the internal energy of the hydrogen atom is

$$\mathfrak{IC} = -\frac{\hbar^2}{2\mu}\left(\frac{\partial^2}{\partial x^2} + \frac{\partial^2}{\partial y^2} + \frac{\partial^2}{\partial z^2}\right) - \frac{e^2}{r}$$

$$= -\frac{\hbar^2}{2\mu}\nabla^2 - \frac{e^2}{r}, \tag{3-10}$$

and Schroedinger's equation has the form

$$\left\{\frac{\hbar^2\nabla^2}{2\mu} + \frac{e^2}{r}\right\}\psi = -E\psi, \tag{3-11}$$

which is to be compared with Eq. (3–9). The value of E, called an eigenvalue, is dependent upon the function ψ.

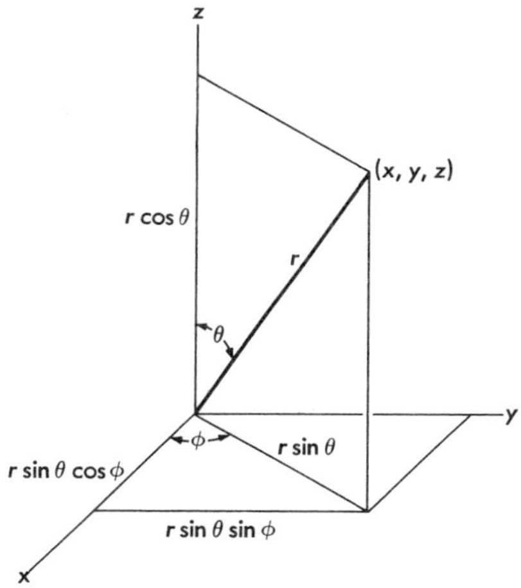

Unfortunately, the choice of cartesian coordinates prevents further mathematical

Fig. 3–1. The spherical coordinate system and its relation to the cartesian coordinate system.

manipulation of Eq. (3–11), and it is necessary to transform the Hamiltonian into spherical coordinates. From Fig. 3–1 it is found that

$$z = r\cos\theta, \qquad x = r\sin\theta\cos\phi, \qquad y = r\sin\theta\sin\phi. \tag{3-12}$$

The transformation of ∇^2 is not difficult but tedious and will not be carried out here. The result which looks formidable, although it is much more tractable, is

$$\mathfrak{IC} = -\frac{\hbar^2}{2\mu}\left[\frac{1}{r^2}\frac{\partial}{\partial r}\left(r^2\frac{\partial}{\partial r}\right) + \frac{1}{r^2\sin\theta}\frac{\partial}{\partial\theta}\left(\sin\theta\frac{\partial}{\partial\theta}\right) + \frac{1}{r^2\sin^2\theta}\frac{\partial^2}{\partial\phi^2}\right] - \frac{e^2}{r}.$$

$$\tag{3-13}$$

Attention is now turned to ψ, which is a function of the coordinates of the system. Two requirements are imposed. They are:

(1) $$\int \psi^*\psi \, d\tau = 1, \tag{3-14}$$

where ψ^* is the complex conjugate of ψ and $d\tau$ is a volume element of the coordinate space. If $\psi^*\psi$ is interpreted as the probability that the electron is in a volume element $d\tau$, then this requirement is simply that the particle must be somewhere in space.

(2)
$$\psi(\phi) = \psi(\phi + 2\pi).$$
(3–15)

This condition is a statement that the function will not change if a rotation about the z-axis by 2π is performed. This requirement is obvious for ordinary spatial coordinates.

To solve $\mathcal{K}\psi = E\psi$, the function $\psi(r, \theta, \phi)$ is assumed to be separable into a product of three functions, each of one variable, in a manner similar to that used for Eq. (2–20):

$$\psi(r, \theta, \phi) = R(r)\Theta(\theta)\Phi(\phi).$$
(3–16a)

If Schroedinger's equation is rewritten using these functions, it has the form

$$\frac{1}{R(r)}\frac{\partial}{\partial r}\left(r^2\frac{\partial R(r)}{\partial r}\right) + \frac{2\mu}{\hbar^2}\left(E + \frac{e^2}{r}\right)r^2$$

$$= -\frac{1}{\Theta(\theta)\Phi(\phi)\sin\theta}\frac{\partial}{\partial\theta}\left(\sin\theta\frac{\partial\Theta(\theta)\Phi(\phi)}{\partial\theta}\right)$$

$$-\frac{1}{\Theta(\theta)\Phi(\phi)\sin^2\theta}\frac{\partial^2\Theta(\theta)\Phi(\phi)}{\partial^2\phi}.$$
(3–16b)

Since the left-hand side of this equation is a function of only r and the right-hand side is a function of only θ and ϕ, the two sides must be equal to a constant. The resulting two equations are

$$\frac{d^2R(r)}{dr^2} + \frac{2}{r}\left(\frac{dR(r)}{dr}\right) + \left[\frac{2\mu}{\hbar^2}\left(E + \frac{e^2}{r}\right) - \frac{\lambda}{r^2}\right]R(r) = 0,$$
(3–17)

where λ is the constant, and

$$\frac{1}{\sin\theta}\frac{\partial}{\partial\theta}\left(\sin\theta\frac{\partial\Theta(\theta)\Phi(\phi)}{\partial\theta}\right) + \frac{1}{\sin^2\theta}\frac{\partial^2\Theta(\theta)\Phi(\phi)}{\partial^2\phi} + \lambda\Theta(\theta)\Phi(\phi) = 0.$$
(3–18)

Again, if Eq. (3–18) is multiplied by $\sin^2\theta/\Theta(\theta)\Phi(\phi)$, the result is separable into two equations, one a function of θ and the other a function of ϕ. They are

$$\frac{d^2\Phi}{d\phi^2} = -m^2\Phi,$$
(3–19)

$$\frac{d^2\Theta}{d\theta^2} + \cot\theta\frac{d\Theta}{d\theta} + \left\{\lambda - \frac{m^2}{\sin^2\theta}\right\}\Theta = 0,$$
(3–20)

where m is a constant.

TABLE 3–1

Solutions of Eq. (3–20) for $l = 0, 1, 2, 3$

$l = 0$	$m = 0$	$\Theta = 1/\sqrt{2}$
$l = 1$	$m = 0$	$\Theta = (\sqrt{3}/2)\cos\theta$
	$m = \pm 1$	$\Theta = \mp(\sqrt{3}/4)\sin\theta$
$l = 2$	$m = 0$	$\Theta = (\sqrt{5}/8)(3\cos^2\theta - 1)$
	$m = \pm 1$	$\Theta = \mp(\sqrt{15}/4)\sin\theta\cos\theta$
	$m = \pm 2$	$\Theta = (\sqrt{15}/16)\sin^2\theta$
$l = 3$	$m = 0$	$\Theta = (\sqrt{63}/8)(5/3\cos^3\theta - \cos\theta)$
	$m = \pm 1$	$\Theta = \mp(\sqrt{21}/32)(5\cos^2\theta - 1)\sin\theta$
	$m = \pm 2$	$\Theta = (\sqrt{105}/16)\sin^2\theta\cos\theta$
	$m = \pm 3$	$\Theta = \mp(\sqrt{35}/32)\sin^3\theta$

Now the solutions of the three equations (3–17), (3–19), and (3–20) depend on the values of m and λ. As an example, Eq. (3–19) has a solution similar to Eq. (2–22) and is

$$\Phi(\phi) = Ae^{im\phi}. \tag{3–21}$$

The allowed values of m are found by using Eq. (3–15), which gives

$$e^{im\phi} = e^{im(\phi+2\pi)}$$

or

$$1 = e^{im2\pi} = \cos 2\pi m + i\sin 2\pi m. \tag{3–22}$$

The only solution to this equation is that m be an integer, i.e., $m = 0, \pm 1, \pm 2, \ldots$ From Eq. (3–14), it is found that $A = (2\pi)^{-1/2}$.

The integration of Eq. (3–20) is less straightforward and will not be calculated here. It is found that solutions are possible only for $\lambda = l(l + 1)$, where l is an integer and $|m| \leq l$. The results for a number of values of l and m are given in Table 3–1.

Equation (3–17) is even more difficult to integrate, and the solutions depend upon whether E is negative or positive. It is found that for any positive value of E, the radial equation may be solved. Thus, all positive E are frequently referred to as the continuum of the energy spectrum.

For the case where E is negative, only certain values of E permit a solution to Eq. (3–17). In particular it is found that the energy is given by

$$E_n = -\frac{2\pi^2\mu e^4}{n^2 h^2}, \tag{3–23}$$

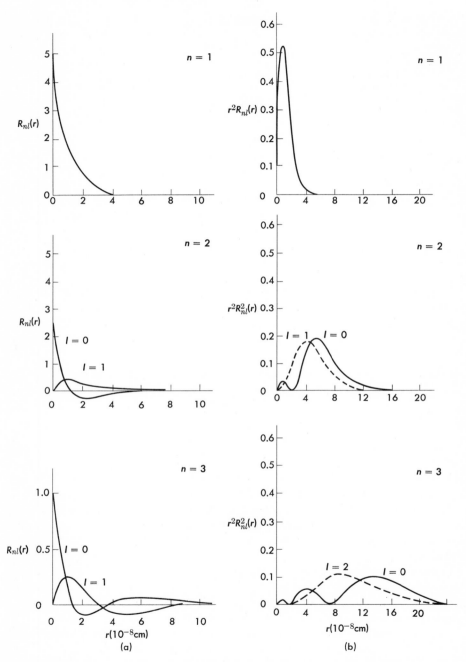

Fig. 3–2. (a) The radial wavefunction $R_{nl}(r)$ vs. the radius r for the three lowest states of hydrogen. (b) The probability of finding an electron between a radius r and $r + dr$ plotted against the radius.

where $n = 1, 2, 3, \ldots$, and $n \geq l + 1$. The number n is called the principal quantum number. The radial wave function belonging to each E is also a function of n and l. For a few of the smaller principal quantum numbers, the radial function is plotted in Fig. 3–2 along with $r^2 R_{nl}^2(r)$. During the discussion of Eq (3–14), it was noted that $r^2 R_{nl}^2(r)$ is the probability that an electron will be in a given radial element. Figure 3–2(b) shows that the electrons are constrained to move in certain narrow ranges of radii. The size of an atom is, therefore, quite diffuse.

If Eq. (3–23) is examined further for the region where E is negative, a number of interesting results are obtained. Since the constants μ, e, and h are known, the energy may be plotted as a function of n. A graph is obtained as shown in Fig. 3–3. The lowest energy state is the *ground* state. It is specified by three integers: $n = 1$, $l = 0$, $m = 0$. Energy states higher than the ground state are called excited states. These states are also specified by three quantum numbers. For instance, the third energy state in Fig. 3–3 is specified by $n = 3$, $l = 0$, $m = 0$. But there are no restrictions on l except that it be less than n. Therefore, besides $l = 0$, we can have $l = 1$ and $l = 2$. Similarly m can have values of -2, -1, 0, $+1$, $+2$ for $l = 2$, and -1, 0, $+1$ for $l = 1$. These nine possible combinations of l and m for $n = 3$ represent different solutions to Schroedinger's equation which have the same energy. Such a state is called a 9-fold degenerate state. In general, if there are n functions which belong to the same energy level, the state is n-fold degenerate.

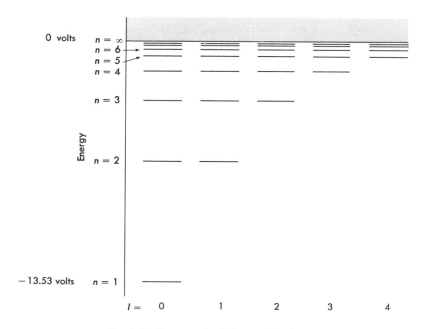

Fig. 3–3. The energy-level diagram of hydrogen.

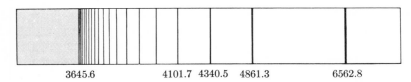

3645.6   4101.7 4340.5 4861.3   6562.8

Fig. 3–4. The spectrum of atomic hydrogen.

When a tube of hydrogen under a low pressure is excited by an electrical spark a red discharge occurs. If the light is passed through a slit and a prism, a series of lines of various colors, including red, are seen. A drawing of this spectrum is shown in Fig. 3–4. These lines were first identified by Balmer in 1885, when he found that they could be fitted to a series of the form

$$\frac{1}{\lambda} = R\left(\frac{1}{2^2} - \frac{1}{n^2}\right), \tag{3–24}$$

where n is an integer greater than 2, λ is the wavelength, and R is a constant called the Rydberg constant.

We may obtain this expression from our energy expression if we assume that the lines observed correspond to the energy radiated as an electron undergoes a transition from a state with $n > 2$ to the state with $n = 2$:

$$\Delta E = h\nu = \frac{2\pi^2\mu e^4}{h^2}\left(\frac{1}{2^2} - \frac{1}{n^2}\right). \tag{3–25}$$

Since spectroscopists use the reciprocal of the wavelength of a line as an energy unit called wave number, we have

$$\tilde{\nu} = \frac{1}{\lambda} = \frac{\nu}{c} = \frac{2\pi^2\mu e^4}{ch^3}\left(\frac{1}{2^2} - \frac{1}{n^2}\right). \tag{3–26}$$

Other series, first observed by Lyman, Paschen, Brackett, and Pfund, change the first integer from 2 to 1, 3, 4, and 5, respectively.

Absorption of energy is the reverse of the process just described. If a continuous spectrum is filtered by a material and then analyzed, there will be wavelength regions where the light is absorbed. These regions correspond to an electron absorbing energy which is a process of going from a lower to higher state.

A notation for the states with various l quantum numbers has been "borrowed" from the spectroscopists. States with $l = 0$ are s-states; $l = 1$ are p-states; $l = 2$, d-states; and $l = 3$, f-states. Fortunately, higher values for l are not common. After f, the letter designations follow alphabetical sequence.

THE ANGULAR WAVE FUNCTIONS

A knowledge of the angular dependence of the solutions of Schroedinger's equation will be necessary in understanding the next chapter. For this reason, we will examine them in more detail.

The azimuthal angle solutions, Φ, are complex functions. Therefore, it is difficult to plot the angular variation of a solution for a given value of l and m. However, there are certain manipulative reasons for conserving this form. The differential equation for Φ, Eq. (3–19), may be written in the form

$$L_\Phi^2 \Phi = m^2 \hbar^2 \Phi, \tag{3-27}$$

if we define the operator $L_\Phi^2 = -\hbar^2(\partial^2/\partial\phi^2)$, or the operator $L_\Phi = (\hbar/i)(\partial/\partial\phi)$. In other words, if a particular solution is known, the operator L_Φ gives immediately the eigenvalue m. It may be shown that the operator L_z which is

$$\frac{\hbar}{i}\left(x\frac{\partial}{\partial y} - y\frac{\partial}{\partial x}\right)$$

is identical to L_Φ, and we will use this more common designation in a later section.

For graphical reasons, it is more convenient to rearrange the solutions of Schroedinger's equation. We have seen that there are nine independent solutions for $n = 3$ which have the same energy. Any combination such as

$$\Psi = a\psi_{n=3,\ l=1,\ m=-1} + b\psi_{n=3,\ l=1,\ m=1} \tag{3-28}$$

is also a solution if we choose a and b so that $\int \Psi^* \Psi \, d\tau = 1$. As an example, let us examine the $n = 3$, $l = 1$ wave functions. In this case, the radial function is the same for each function, and so we may neglect it. The angular functions, $Y_l^m = \Theta_{l,m}\Phi_m$, are

$$Y_{l=1}^{m=1} = \frac{-\sqrt{3}}{4} \sin\theta \left(\frac{1}{2\pi}\right)^{1/2} e^{i\phi},$$

$$Y_{l=1}^{m=0} = \frac{\sqrt{3}}{2} \cos\theta \left(\frac{1}{2\pi}\right)^{1/2}, \tag{3-29}$$

$$Y_{l=1}^{m=-1} = \frac{\sqrt{3}}{4} \sin\theta \left(\frac{1}{2\pi}\right)^{1/2} e^{-i\phi}.$$

A convenient choice for a linear combination is

$$p_x \approx Y_1^1 - Y_1^{-1} \approx \sin\theta \cos\phi = x,$$

$$p_y \approx Y_1^1 + Y_1^{-1} \approx \sin\theta \sin\phi = y, \tag{3-30}$$

$$p_z \approx Y_1^0 \approx \cos\theta = z,$$

where the numerical coefficients have been omitted for simplicity.

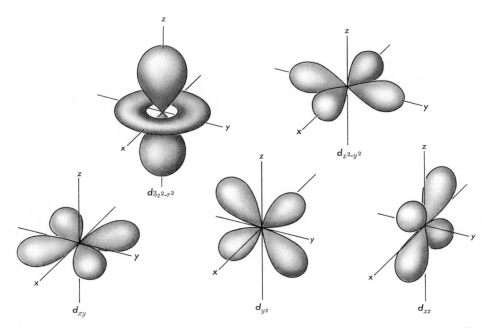

Fig. 3–5. The angular distribution of the hydrogenic wave functions for $l = 2$. The plots are contour diagrams for a constant value of the radial wave function.

The student will recognize that these linear combinations are just the components of a unit vector in a spherical coordinate system. For the $l = 2$ functions, a convenient choice is

$$d_{3z^2-r^2} \approx Y_2^0 \approx 3z^2 - r^2,$$

$$d_{x^2-y^2} \approx Y_2^2 + Y_2^{-2} \approx x^2 - y^2,$$

$$d_{xy} \approx Y_2^2 - Y_2^{-2} \approx xy, \tag{3–31}$$

$$d_{xz} \approx Y_1^1 + Y_1^{-1} \approx xz,$$

$$d_{yz} \approx Y_1^1 - Y_1^{-1} \approx yz.$$

A plot of these angular functions is shown in Fig. 3–5.

THE APPLICATION OF ELECTRIC AND MAGNETIC FIELDS

It may be asked how one knows from the spectrum of an element that there are nine functions which belong to the energy level for $n = 3$. The answer is that as the resolution of a spectrograph is increased, each line observed under low resolution consists of several lines. It is found, for instance, that the yellow line of mercury has the structure shown in Fig. 3–6. An analysis of this "fine structure" enables the spectroscopist to characterize the closely spaced energy levels. In other words, a more refined theory shows that the energy, although mainly dependent upon n, is also dependent upon l.

But still there is a degeneracy due to m. To observe this, we must apply a magnetic field to the emitting or absorbing system. This raises another question. What happens to an atomic system when an external electric or magnetic field is applied? To answer this question, we return to a consideration of symmetry.

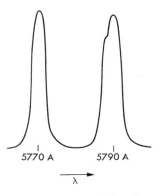

Fig. 3–6. A diagram of the yellow doublet of Mercury.

A free atom Hamiltonian has spherical symmetry. The potential has a $1/r$ dependence which is clearly spherically symmetric. The ∇^2-term has the same symmetry, although it is not so obvious as the potential term. If an external field is applied, the symmetry of the Hamiltonian is no longer spherical. The Hamiltonian includes the symmetry of the external field. If an electric field is applied to an atom in the z-direction, the Hamiltonian of Eq. (3–13) has added the potential energy of the electron in the field. This additional term, called a perturbing potential, is

$$\mathcal{3C}' = ezE_z = er\cos\theta E_z, \tag{3–32}$$

where E is the electric field strength. The total Hamiltonian now has a preferred direction, namely the z-axis, where $\mathcal{3C}'$ is a maximum. More generally, the perturbing Hamiltonian for an arbitrary direction is

$$\mathcal{3C}' = e\mathbf{r} \cdot \mathbf{E}, \tag{3–33}$$

which classically is the energy of an electric dipole $e\mathbf{r}$ in an electric field $\mathbf{E}$.

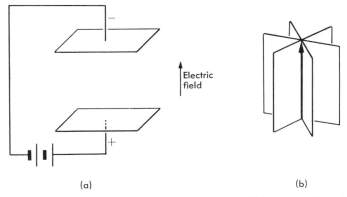

Electric field

(a)   (b)

Fig. 3–7. (a) A diagram illustrating the application of an electric field by means of parallel plates connected to a battery. (b) A diagram showing three possible mirror planes of symmetry.

Figure 3–7 shows that an electric field reduces the symmetry to that of an arrow. That is, all planes which contain the arrow are symmetry planes. This may be seen by considering the electric field as produced by a pair of charged parallel plates perpendicular to the z-axis, as shown in Fig. 3–7(a). Any reflection plane containing the z-axis must leave the situation unchanged; but if a reflection perpendicular to the z-axis is considered, the sign of E changes, and consequently the plane is not a symmetry plane.

The symmetry which results from the application of a magnetic field is different from that produced by an electric field because a magnetic field results from a rotation of electric charge. Any change in the sense of rotation changes the direction of $\mathbf{H}$. Figure 3–8 shows that if $\mathbf{H}$ is along the z-axis, any reflection in a plane containing $\mathbf{H}$ will reverse the direction of charge rotation and thus will change the sign of the field. In contrast, a reflection in a plane perpendicular to $\mathbf{H}$ will not change the field but will maintain the same sense of rotation of the charge which produces the field. Therefore, a magnetic field reduces the symmetry of the system to that of a reflection plane perpendicular to the field.

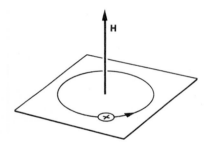

Fig. 3–8. A diagram showing a magnetic field arising from a circulating charge. The mirror plane shown does not change the direction of rotation, but any other nonparallel reflection will cause a change.

To see the effect of an electric field on an atom, let us consider a p-electron moving in an electric field having the symmetry of an arrow. A state associated with a p-electron has, as shown before, 3-fold degeneracy, which corresponds to the three functions x, y, and z multiplied by a radial function. Let the electric field be along the z-axis. From Fig. 3–8 it is apparent that a reflection in any plane containing the electric field leaves the p_z-orbital unchanged. However, the p_x- and p_y-orbitals are transformed into each other. In particular, if a reflection is made at an angle of $\phi = \pi/4$, then p_x is transformed into a p_y-orbital, and p_y into a p_x-orbital. In other words, the electric field has removed the equivalence of the p_z-orbital to the p_y- and p_x-orbitals.

Since the Hamiltonian must have the symmetry of the system, it is expected that if $\math3C$ operates on p_z, an energy will be obtained which will differ from the case of $\math3C$ operating on p_x or p_y or a linear combination of p_x and p_y. The operation of $\math3C$ on p_x or p_y will give the same energy. This is seen by noting that if $\math3C p_x = E_{p_x} p_x$, then a reflection in the plane in Fig. 3–9 gives $\math3C p_y = E_{p_x} p_y$, since $\math3C$ is invariant. But since $\math3C p_y = E_{p_y} p_y$, then $E_{p_x} = E_{p_y}$. In other words, a 3-fold p-state is split by an electric field into a singlet and a doublet state. In general, the application of any electric field reduces the degeneracy of a state. Of course,

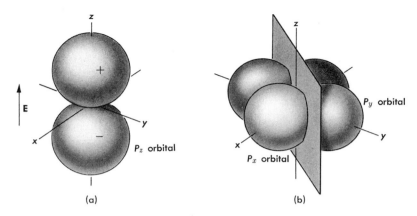

Fig. 3–9. (a) A diagram showing that the symmetry of a p_z-orbital is unaffected by an electric field paralle to the z-axis. (b) A diagram showing that mirror plane containing the z-axis and at an angle $\varphi = \pi/4$ changes a p_x-orbital into a p_y-orbital and vice versa.

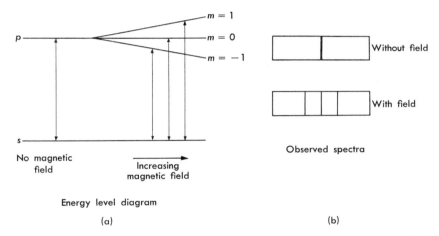

Fig. 3–10. (a) The Zeeman effect for s- and p-states assuming no-spin angular momentum. (b) The corresponding spectra observed with and without a magnetic field.

an s-state has no orbital degeneracy and so is not affected by an electric field. It is possible to show from symmetry arguments alone that any orbital state can have no more than 3-fold degeneracy in an external electric field.

The situation for a magnetic field is similar to the electric-field case except that all degeneracy is removed. A reflection in a plane perpendicular to the magnetic field changes p_x into itself, p_y into itself, and p_z into $-p_z$. Thus, each orbital transforms into itself only, and all the degeneracy is removed. In Fig. 3–10 the results are depicted for an s-to-p transition both in the absence and in the presence of a magnetic field. It shows that in a magnetic field the single absorption line is split into three lines. This splitting is called the Zeeman effect.

ELECTRON SPIN

The actual observation of a Zeeman effect shows generally a more complicated spectrum than that described in Fig. 3–10. More lines are observed than can be accounted for. The solution to this problem was suggested by Pauli and by Goudsmit and Uhlenbeck. The data can be fitted if it is assumed that there exists a fourth quantum number which is associated with the electron and is attributed to the electron having a magnetic dipole moment. This quantum number is known as the electron-spin angular-momentum quantum number. It is designated by the letter s and has a value of $\frac{1}{2}\hbar$. Similar to l, s has components, m_s, which are either $\pm\frac{1}{2}\hbar$. That is, each spin state is 2-fold degenerate, and the degeneracy is removed with a magnetic field. A modified picture of an s-to-p transition for a single electron is shown in Fig. 3–11. Some of the possible twelve lines do not occur because of restrictions on angular-momentum changes, and only ten lines are actually observed. Nevertheless, Zeeman analysis gives detailed information about the states involved in the transition.

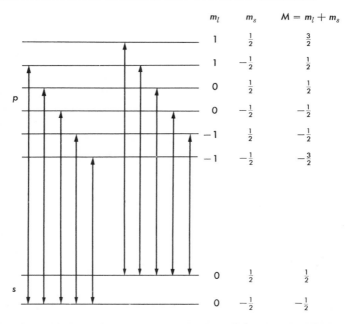

Fig. 3–11. The allowed transitions of an s–p transition in the limit of high magnetic field where any coupling of the spin angular momentum to the orbital angular momentum is relatively small.

GROUND-STATE CONFIGURATIONS OF ATOMS

The previous discussion has dealt only with atoms of hydrogenic type. To solve the many-electron problem approximate methods must be used because not only are there interactions between the nucleus and the electrons but there are repulsive interactions between electrons. As an example, we can count the number of repulsive terms for a five-electron atom. The first electron interacts with the four other electrons. Another electron interacts with four electrons also, but one interaction has already been counted. Therefore, there are only three new interactions. For the five electrons, there are a total of ten repulsive terms which must be put in the Hamiltonian. It is easy to see that the computation difficulties have increased enormously and that approximations must be made.

A first approximation is that each electron has a hydrogenic-type orbital and can be described by four quantum numbers: n, l, m_l, and m_s. In other words, we assume that each electron moves in approximately a spherical potential. It is necessary at this point to introduce a restriction on the number of electrons in an atom with the same four quantum numbers. Like many of the fundamental physical principles, it is a statement of something which cannot be done. The Pauli exclusion principle states in simple form that no two electrons in an atom may have the same four quantum numbers. This statement is found to be obeyed by nature, but as yet cannot be derived from other "first" principles.

The application of the Pauli exclusion principle to atomic systems is illustrated in the following examples. For hydrogen, there is only one electron which may exist in any orbital, but the one with the lowest energy is the $n = 1$, $l = 0$ orbital or, in brief, the $1s$ configuration. For helium with two electrons, the ground state may be described by $1s^2$, which means that for both electrons $n = 1$, $l = 0$, $m = 0$, but one electron has $m_s = +\frac{1}{2}$ and the other has $m_s = -\frac{1}{2}$. In general, the configuration is specified by a symbol of the form nl^x, where n is the principal quantum number, l is the orbital angular-momentum quantum number, and x is the number of electrons with those quantum numbers. The Pauli principle limits the number of electrons with $n = 1$ to two. For Li the configuration must be $1s^22s$, and for Be, $1s^22s^2$. Again only two electrons can have $n = 2$, $l = 0$, so that boron, the next element in the periodic table, must have $n = 2$, $l = 1$. With these quantum numbers, six electrons may be designated using combinations of $m_l = 1$, 0, -1, and $m_s = \pm\frac{1}{2}$. Thus the ground-state configuration of boron is $1s^22s^22p^1$. Carbon has the configuration $1s^22s^22p^2$. Neon has the configuration $1s^22s^22p^6$, which uses all possible combinations for $n = 1$ and $n = 2$. Sodium must have the configuration $1s^22s^22p^63s^1$ or (Ne) $3s^1$. The process is continued for argon with the configuration (Ne) $3s^23p^6$.

It might be expected that after argon the $n = 3$, $l = 2$ orbitals would fill up, but the energy of these levels is still higher than the $4s$ level at atomic numbers of about 20. Thus the configuration of potassium is (Ar) $4s^1$ and that of calcium is (Ar) $4s^2$. With scandium the $3d$ level becomes lowest with the result that its configuration is (Ar) $4s^23d^1$. There are 10 d-electrons possible. The elements with configurations with $3d$ electrons are the first transition series. After the $3d$ electrons are filled, the next level is the $4p$-level.

TABLE 3–2. The Periodic Table

with Ground-State Configurations of the Elements

First period	1 H $1s^1$									
Second period He +	3 Li $2s^1$	4 Be $2s^2$								
Third period Ne +	11 Na $3s^1$	12 Mg $3s^2$								
Fourth period Ar +	19 K $4s^1$	20 Ca $4s^2$	21 Sc $4s^23d^1$	22 Ti $4s^23d^2$	23 V $4s^23d^3$	24 Cr $4s^13d^5$	25 Mn $4s^23d^5$	26 Fe $4s^23d^6$	27 Co $4s^23d^7$	28 Ni $4s^23d^8$
Fifth period Kr +	37 Rb $5s^1$	38 Sr $5s^2$	39 Y $5s^24d^1$	40 Zr $5s^24d^2$	41 Nb $5s^14d^4$	42 Mo $5s^14d^5$	43 Tc $5s^24d^5$	44 Ru $5s^14d^7$	45 Rh $5s^14d^8$	46 Pd $4d^{10}$
Sixth period Xe +	55 Cs $6s^1$	56 Ba $6s^2$	57* La $6s^25d^1$	72 Hf $6s^24f^{14}5d^2$	73 Ta $6s^24f^{14}5d^3$	74 W $6s^24f^{14}5d^4$	75 Re $6s^24f^{14}5d^5$	76 Os $6s^24f^{14}5d^6$	77 Ir $6s^24f^{14}5d^7$	78 Pt $6s^14f^{14}5d^9$
Seventh period Rn +	87 Fr $7s^1$	88 Ra $7s^2$	89† Ac $7s^26d^1$							

*Rare earths or Lanthanides Xe +	57 La $6s^25d^1$	58 Ce $6s^25d^14f^1$	59 Pr $6s^25d^14f^2$	60 Nd $6s^25d^14f^3$	61 Pm $6s^25d^14f^4$

†Actinides Rn +	89 Ac $7s^26d^1$	90 Th $7s^26d^2$	91 Pa $7s^26d^15f^2$	92 U $7s^26d^15f^3$	93 Np $7s^26d^15f^4$

The sequence is repeated in the fifth row of the periodic table. In the sixth row after barium, the $4f$ level becomes the next lowest energy level. With $n = 4$, $l = 3$, there are fourteen possible combinations of m_l and m_s. Therefore, the rare-earth elements have ground-state configurations involving f electrons. In the seventh row after radium a similar event occurs which corresponds to the use of $5f$-orbitals in the actinide series.

Table 3–2 gives the electronic ground-state configuration for each element of the periodic table. A convenient mnemonic device is shown in Fig. 3–12. Although there are some exceptions, the device gives almost all ground-state configurations correctly.

								2 He $1s^2$
		5 B $2s^22p^1$	6 C $2s^22p^2$	7 N $2s^22p^3$	8 O $2s^22p^4$	9 F $2s^22p^5$	10 Ne $2s^22p^6$	
		13 Al $3s^23p^1$	14 Si $3s^23p^2$	15 P $3s^23p^3$	16 S $3s^23p^4$	17 Cl $3s^23p^5$	18 Ar $3s^23p^6$	
29 Cu $4s^13d^{10}$	30 Zn $4s^23d^{10}$	31 Ga $4s^23d^{10}4p^1$	32 Ge $4s^23d^{10}4p^2$	33 As $4s^23d^{10}4p^3$	34 Se $4s^23d^{10}4p^4$	35 Br $4s^23d^{10}4p^5$	36 Kr $4s^23d^{10}4p^6$	
47 Ag $5s^14d^{10}$	48 Cd $5s^24d^{10}$	49 In $5s^24d^{10}5p^1$	50 Sn $5s^24d^{10}5p^2$	51 Sb $5s^24d^{10}5p^3$	52 Te $5s^24d^{10}5p^4$	53 I $5s^24d^{10}5p^5$	54 Xe $5s^24d^{10}5p^6$	
79 Au $14f^{14}5d^{10}$	80 Hg $6s^24f^{14}5d^{10}$	81 Tl $6s^24f^{14}5d^{10}6p^1$	82 Pb $6s^24f^{14}5d^{10}6p^2$	83 Bi $6s^24f^{14}5d^{10}6p^3$	84 Po $6s^24f^{14}5d^{10}6p^4$	85 At $6s^24f^{14}5d^{10}6p^5$	86 Rn $6s^24f^{14}5d^{10}6p^5$	

62 Sm $6s^25d^14f^5$	63 Eu $6s^25d^14f^6$	64 Gd $6s^25d^14f^7$	65 Tb $6s^25d^14f^8$	66 Dy $6s^25d^14f^9$	67 Ho $6s^25d^14f^{10}$	68 Er $6s^25d^14f^{11}$	69 Tm $6s^25d^14f^{12}$	70 Yb $6s^25d^14f^{13}$	71 Lu $6s^25d^14f^{14}$

94 Pu $7s^25f^6$	95 Am $7s^25f^7$	96 Cm $7s^26d^15f^7$	97 Bk $7s^26d^15f^8$	98 Cf $7s^25f^{10}$	99 Es $7s^25f^{11}$	100 Fm $7s^25f^{12}$	101 Md $7s^25f^{13}$	102 No $7s^25f^{14}$	103 Lw $7s^26d^15f^{14}$

To find the electron configuration for an ion from the elemental configuration, it is necessary to observe only a few rules. The s-electrons with highest principal quantum number are lost first in ionization. The next electrons are those which would be lost if the atomic number were decreased. A few examples illustrate these rules.

$$\text{Al}^0: \quad 1s^22s^22p^63s^23p^1 \qquad \text{Al}^{3+}: \quad 1s^22s^22p^6$$

$$\text{V}^0: \quad (\text{Ar})\, 3d^34s^2 \qquad \begin{cases} \text{V}^{2+}: & (\text{Ar})\, 3d^3 \\ \text{V}^{3+}: & (\text{Ar})\, 3d^2 \end{cases}$$

$$\text{Nd}^0: \quad (\text{Xe})\, 4f^46s^2 \qquad \text{Nd}^{3+}: \quad (\text{Xe})\, 4f^3$$

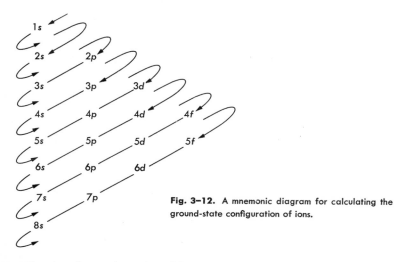

Fig. 3–12. A mnemonic diagram for calculating the ground-state configuration of ions.

For negative ion formation, the additional electrons are added in sequence as though one were considering atoms of higher atomic number.

$$N^{3-}: \quad 1s^2 2s^2 2p^6$$
$$I^-: \quad (Kr)\ 5s^2 4d^{10} 5p^6$$

THE GROUND-STATE TERMS FOR MANY-ELECTRON ATOMS

In the following chapter, we will need to know the spatial electron distribution for many-electron ions. In general it will be difficult to determine the radial extent, but it is possible to construct the angular distribution from a knowledge of the electron configuration, which gives us the possibilities for the single-electron angular wave function.

TABLE 3–3

M_L	$M_s = 1$	$M_s = 0$	$M_s = -1$
2		$\{1, -\frac{1}{2}\}\{1, \frac{1}{2}\}$	
1	$\{1, \frac{1}{2}\}\{0, \frac{1}{2}\}$	$\{1, -\frac{1}{2}\}\{0, \frac{1}{2}\};\ \{0, -\frac{1}{2}\}\{1, \frac{1}{2}\}$	$\{1, -\frac{1}{2}\}\{0, -\frac{1}{2}\}$
0	$\{1, +\frac{1}{2}\}\{-1, \frac{1}{2}\}$	$\{1, -\frac{1}{2}\}\{-1, \frac{1}{2}\};\ \{0, -\frac{1}{2}\}\{0, \frac{1}{2}\};\ \{-1, -\frac{1}{2}\}\{1, \frac{1}{2}\}$	$\{1, -\frac{1}{2}\}\{-1, -\frac{1}{2}\}$
-1	$\{-1, \frac{1}{2}\}\{0, \frac{1}{2}\}$	$\{-1, -\frac{1}{2}\}\{0, \frac{1}{2}\};\ \{0, -\frac{1}{2}\}\{-1, \frac{1}{2}\}$	$\{-1, -\frac{1}{2}\}\{0, -\frac{1}{2}\}$
-2		$\{-1, -\frac{1}{2}\}\{-1, \frac{1}{2}\}$	

Let us consider the configuration $2p^2$. We may write the wave function symbolically as the product $\{m_l, m_s\}_1 \{m_l, m_s\}_2$, where we have omitted the values of n and l because they are fixed. There are various possibilities of products consistent with the Pauli exclusion principle. They are listed in Table 3–3. Since the electrons are indistinguishable, only different wave functions are listed.

Let us define a new operator, called the total orbital angular-momentum operator, $\mathbf{L}$, as

$$\mathbf{L} = \sum_i \mathbf{L}_i, \qquad (3\text{--}34)$$

where $\mathbf{L}_i$ operates only on the ith electron. Similarly, the total-spin angular-momentum operator may also be defined as

$$\mathbf{S} = \sum_i \mathbf{S}_i, \qquad (3\text{--}35)$$

and the z-components of these operators as

$$L_z = \sum_i L_{iz}; \qquad S_z = \sum_i S_{iz}. \qquad (3\text{--}36)$$

The reason for doing this is that as in Eq. (3–27), L_z and S_z must give the total magnetic quantum numbers when they operate on the wave functions of Table 3–3.

As an example, if we operate on $\{1, -\frac{1}{2}\} \{, \frac{1}{2}\}$ with L_z, we obtain

$$
\begin{aligned}
L_z \{1, -\tfrac{1}{2}\} \{1, \tfrac{1}{2}\} &= (L_{z_1} + L_{z_2}) \{1, -\tfrac{1}{2}\} \{1, \tfrac{1}{2}\} \\
&= (1 + 1) \{1, -\tfrac{1}{2}\} \{1, \tfrac{1}{2}\}, \\
&= (2) \{1, -\tfrac{1}{2}\} \{1, \tfrac{1}{2}\},
\end{aligned}
$$

where L_{z_i} operates on only the ith electron. In general we see that

$$
\begin{aligned}
L_z \{m_1, -\tfrac{1}{2}\} \{m_2, \tfrac{1}{2}\} &= (m_1 + m_2) \{m_1, -\tfrac{1}{2}\} \{m_2, \tfrac{1}{2}\} \\
&= M_L \{m_1, -\tfrac{1}{2}\} \{m_2, \tfrac{1}{2}\}.
\end{aligned}
$$

In a similar manner we may define $M_S \equiv \sum_i m_{s_i}$ and find that for the state $\{1, -\frac{1}{2}\} \{1, \frac{1}{2}\}$ we have $M_S = 0$ and $M_L = 2$. There are other functions which give $M_S = 0$, but have $M_L = 1, 0, -1$, and -2. Since the maximum value of M_L is 2, we have $L = 2$ and similarly $S = 0$. Therefore, these five states have the same angular momentum properties as a d-state with zero electron spin. The set of such states is called a term and is designated by the symbol ^{2S+1}L. In our example, the $L = 2$, $S = 0$ state is written as ^1D and read as a "singlet d-state."

So far only five of the fifteen functions in Table 3–3 have been used. We can choose one of the remaining functions and see what values of M_S and M_L are obtained. A convenient choice is $\{1, \frac{1}{2}\} \{0, \frac{1}{2}\}$ because $M_S = 1$, a maximum value. The largest value of M_L with $M_S = 1$ is 1. We can find eight other functions which form the set for $M_S = 1, 0, -1$ and $M_L = 1, 0, -1$. Consequently, these functions belong to a ^3P state. In Table 3–3 we are left with one function, for instance $\{0, \frac{1}{2}\} \{0, -\frac{1}{2}\}$, which has $M_S = 0$, $M_L = 0$ and is simply a ^1S state.

TABLE 3–4

THE GROUND-STATE TERMS AND CONFIGURATIONS OF SOME COMMON
TRANSITION METAL IONS

Term	Configuration	IONS		
		Divalent	Trivalent	Tetravalent
^2D	d^1	Sc^{2+}	Ti^{3+}, Zr^{3+}	V^{4+}
^3F	d^2		V^{3+}	Cr^{4+}, Mo^{4+}
^4F	d^3	V^{2+}	Cr^{3+}, Mo^{3+}	Te^{4+}, Re^{4+}
^5D	d^4	Cr^{2+}	Mn^{3+}	Ru^{4+}, Os^{4+}
^6S	d^5	Mn^{2+}	Fe^{3+}, Ru^{3+}, Os^{3+}	Ir^{4+}
^5D	d^6	Fe^{2+}, Ru^{2+}, Os^{2+}	Co^{3+}, Rh^{3+}, Ir^{3+}	Pd^{4+}, Pt^{4+}, Ni^{4+}
^4F	d^7	Co^{2+}	Ni^{3+}	
^3F	d^8	Ni^{2+}		
^2D	d^9	Cu^{2+}, Ag^{2+}		

With this method we have found that a $2p^2$ configuration gives rise to three terms: ^1D, ^3P, and ^1S. Since the symmetry as denoted by the value of L of the various terms is different, we may anticipate that the energy of each term, and thus of the states belonging to the term, is different.

The energy of the terms of a given configuration may be calculated by means of quantum mechanics. However, to find the lowest term it is sufficient to use the following set of rules, which were first formulated by Hund. The state with lowest energy is that with (1) maximum spin angular momentum and (2) maximum orbital angular momentum consistent with the Pauli exclusion principle. Thus the lowest term of a p^2 configuration is ^3P state.

It is not necessary to write out a table such as Table 3–3 every time one wishes to calculate the lowest term of a configuration. Hund's rules provide the method. As an example, consider a d^6 configuration. Only five electrons may be placed in a d-shell without pairing so that there must be one electron pair. The maximum value of $M_S = 5(\frac{1}{2}) + (-\frac{1}{2}) = 2$, and therefore $S = 2$. The maximum value of M_L consistent with the spin requirement is $2 + 1 + 0 - 1 - 2 + 2 = 2$, and therefore the lowest state for a d^6 configuration is ^5D. A list of Hund ground states is given in Table 3–4.

The basis for Hund's rules is essentially electrostatic repulsion. The farther the electrons are from each other, the smaller the repulsion. It may be shown from the exclusion principle and a quantum-mechanical calculation that there is zero probability of finding two electrons with the same spin simultaneously at the same point in space. Thus, the exclusion principle automatically keeps electrons with parallel spins out of each other's way, which accounts for the first requirement.

The second requirement that L be a maximum is also a result of electrostatic repulsion. It should be recalled from Chapter 2 that the function $e^{im\phi}$ is a rotation operator. It rotates any function, which in our context here is the θ- and r-dependent wave functions. If it is required that electrons remain as far apart as possible, they should rotate about the nucleus in the same direction because opposite directions bring them near to each other on each revolution. Therefore, individual m_l for each electron will have as nearly as possible the same sign, and M_L will be a maximum; L is, by definition, the maximum value of M_L.

REFERENCES

CARTMELL, E., and G. W. A. FOWLES, *Valency and Molecular Structure*, Butterworths, London, 1956.

COULSON, C. A., *Valence*, Oxford, New York, 1961.

HARVEY, K. B., and G. B. PORTER, *Introduction to Physical Inorganic Chemistry*, Addison-Wesley, Reading, Mass., 1963.

HEITLER, W., *Elementary Wave Mechanics*, Oxford, New York, 1956.

HERZBERG, G., *Atomic Spectra and Atomic Structure*, Dover, New York, 1944.

ROJANSKY, V., *Introductory Quantum Mechanics*, Prentice-Hall, Englewood Cliffs, N. J., 1938.

PROBLEMS

1. Show that Eq. (3–7) is true by substitution of Eqs. (3–3) through (3–6) into Eq. (3–2).

2. Calculate the ground-state terms of the f^n configurations.

3. Calculate the wavelength of the $n = 2$ to $n = 1$ transition of hydrogen. Compare your result with a handbook value.

4. What are the ground-state configurations of Ti^{2+}, P^{3-}, Xe^{4+}, Ra^{2+}, U^{3+}, Hf^{4+}, Mn^{2+}, Se^{2-}, and Cu^{1+}?

5. Consider two electrons in an sp-configuration. What are the possible terms arising from this system?

6. (a) Consider an operator P that changes a wave function $\psi(x, y, z)$ into $\psi(-x, -y, -z)$. If ψ is written in spherical coordinates, what operation on r, θ, and ϕ occurs when P is applied?
   (b) Show that $PY_1^m = -Y_1^m$ and $PY_2^m = Y_2^m$ for all values of m. The operator P is known as the parity operator.

7. What is the value of kT in wave numbers for $T = 1°K$?

8. Show that the linear combinations of spherical harmonics of Eq. (3–31) have the cartesian form indicated.

9. Draw graphs of p_x^2, p_y^2, and p_z^2 using polar graph paper. For the p_x- and p_y-plots it is convenient to choose $\theta = \pi/2$ first and to draw a contour map for a couple of other angles of θ. Since the square of p_x, p_y, or p_z is the probability of finding an electron in a volume element, the resulting graphs are contour maps of electron density at a given radius.

10. The energy required for the removal of an electron from an atom is called the ionization energy. Calculate the value of this quantity for hydrogen in electron volts. Calculate the ionization energy for the $2s$ electron of lithium, and compare with the handbook value. What may be the cause of the discrepancy?

4

Coordination Compounds

If an ion such as Ti^{3+} is dissolved in a crystal of $AlCl_3$, the ion is no longer a free ion as considered in the previous chapter, but it has additional forces due to the electric fields of the chloride and aluminum ions which surround it. Very often in chemistry, these forces are strong enough to cause an ion and its immediate surroundings to act as a unit in chemical reactions. Such units are called coordination compounds.

It should be obvious that there is a range of forces possible and that a given ion may form tightly bound complexes with some molecules and loosely bound complexes with others. Since the line between these extremes is so diffuse, it is proposed that whenever an ion is placed in a solution or crystal, it forms to a greater or lesser extent a coordination compound.

The simplest coordination compound is that of a singly charged S-state ion in solution. Here the central metal ion has spherical symmetry and the interaction with the neighboring molecules is simply coulombic. The compound may be approximated by a point charge surrounded by dipoles or other point charges at a distance equal to the radius sum of the ion and adjacent molecule. In other words, this case is just that of an ion in a crystal lattice with the exception that there is only one ion interacting with nearest neighbors.

If we consider a central ion which has a ground state with orbital angular momentum, we have a situation which is more complex. The electric fields which the surrounding ions produce will remove some of the degeneracy of the free-ion energy levels. This case is extremely common in the $3d$-, $4d$-, and $5d$-transition series as well as in the lanthanide and actinide series of the periodic table. It is with these groups that this chapter will deal.

CHEMICAL PROPERTIES OF COORDINATION COMPOUNDS

If air is bubbled through a solution of NH_3 and $CoCl_2$ in water to which has been added some charcoal as a catalyst, a yellow crystalline compound is formed. A chemical analysis shows that the composition is $CoCl_3(NH_3)_6$. When it is treated with concentrated sulfuric acid, no ammonium ion is formed but the chloride is replaced by sulfate. Hot HCl has no effect on the NH_3. All chloride ions may be precipitated with silver nitrate.

If the conductivity of a solution of the salt is measured and compared with the equivalent conductivity of NaCl, $BaCl_2$, and $AlCl_3$, it may be inferred that there are four ions per molecule formed upon solution in water. If the freezing-point depression of water is measured, the result is also in agreement with the solution containing four ions per molecule dissolved.

From the preparation of $CoCl_3(NH_3)_6$ one can also obtain a second salt which has a red color and the formula $CoCl_3(NH_3)_5(H_2O)$. Likewise, this material gives four ions per molecule in a water solution. If $CoCl_3(NH_3)_5H_2O$ is dehydrated, a darker red material is formed with the composition $CoCl_3(NH_3)_5$. Conductivity measurements show that for this compound there are only three ions per molecule in a water solution. A silver chloride precipitation yields only two moles of Cl^- per formula weight. Thus one chloride is more stable than the others.

These reactions and many similar reactions were studied by Alfred Werner in the early part of the twentieth century. Because x-ray techniques and instruments had not been discovered, he relied on chemical methods to determine the structure of these compounds. Werner proposed that all these reactions were explainable if it were assumed that each cobalt ion was surrounded by six equivalent sites which could be occupied by NH_3, H_2O, Cl^-, or other groups. In addition, the molecules in these sites had bonds to the cation that are stronger than normal valence bonds.

The question arises as to how these sites are arranged about the metal ion. By geometrical examination, it is easy to show that six equivalent sites may be arranged in only three ways about a central point. These possibilities are shown in Fig. 4–1.

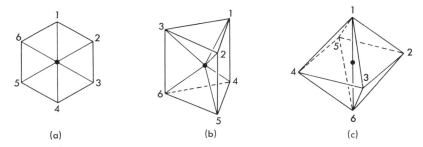

Fig. 4–1. The three possible ways of distributing six equivalent points about a central point.

How can one differentiate between these cases by chemical means? A first thought might be to replace one of the ammonia molecules in $CoCl_3(NH_3)_6$ with a water molecule or other group, but it is not difficult to see from Fig. 4–1 that no new characteristic is evident which may be used. However, if a compound of the form $Co(NH_3)_4(H_2O)_2Cl_3$ is made, a differentiation is possible because of the various stereoisomers which are formed. In the hexagon case, the water molecules may be substituted on any of these positions: (1, 2), (1, 3), or (1, 4). In a similar manner for the trigonal prism, substitutions are possible at (1, 2), (1, 4), and (1, 5) to give different isomers. But the regular octahedron

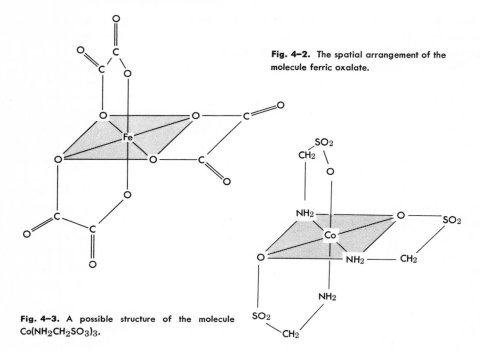

Fig. 4-2. The spatial arrangement of the molecule ferric oxalate.

Fig. 4-3. A possible structure of the molecule Co(NH$_2$CH$_2$SO$_3$)$_3$.

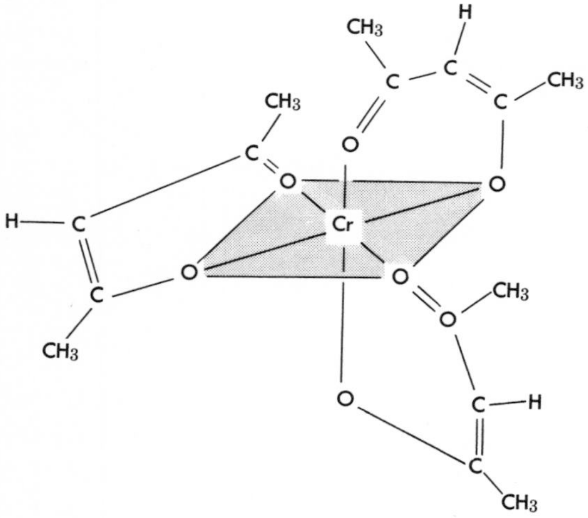

Fig. 4-4. The structure of chromium (III) acetylacetonate.

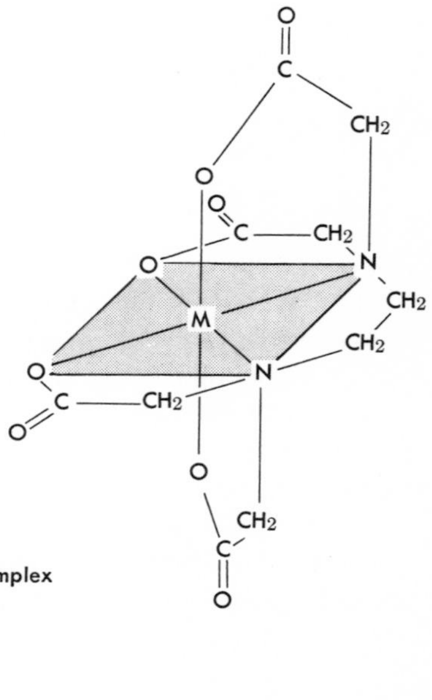

Fig. 4-5. A structure of a hexadentate complex with EDTA.

gives only two distinct arrangements: (1, 2) or (1, 6). Werner was able to isolate only two stereoisomers and thus was able to postulate the octahedral model for cobalt complexes.

This discussion raises a point which is often ignored by chemists. It is that structural determination by default is not reliable. One may argue that the structure could still be either the hexagonal or trigonal prismatic structure but that one of the isomeric possibilities is unstable and transforms into another during the isolation. In such a case, only two isomers would be discovered which would lead to erroneous conclusions about the true structure. Werner had at his disposal, however, a multitude of other data which supported his contention.

LIGAND TYPES

We have mentioned several ions or molecules which coordinate metal ions. Such groups are called *ligands*. Besides those listed, other simple ions such as NO_3^-, NO, pseudohalides, hydroxyl, and carbonate are but a few of the possibilities. These ligands occupy only one coordination position in contrast to others which may use two or more sites.

When ferric ion is reacted with oxalic acid, a green crystalline material precipitates out of concentrated solutions. The formula is $K_3Fe(C_2O_4)_3 \cdot 3H_2O$. This compound is an example of a single ligand coordinating a metal ion at two sites. Figure 4–2 shows the arrangement. The oxalate ion is called a bidentate group. To form a stable bidentate structure, the resulting ring must have five or six members because of the spatial requirements. The only known compounds have adjacent coordination positions occupied by the bidentate ligand.

The oxalate ion is an example of a ligand with both ends of the molecule ionized. It is also possible to form bidentate ligands with neither end ionized. An example of the latter is ethylenediamine, $NH_2CH_2CH_2NH_2$. The bonding between such a ligand and the metal ion is a covalent bond with the nitrogens donating a pair of electrons.

Mixed bonding ligands are also found. For example, in amino-methylsulfonate, $^-O—SO_2—CH_2—NH_2$, the nitrogen donates electrons to the metal ion and the ionic sulfonate—metal bond becomes more covalent. Such a ligand is called a *chelating* agent. The structure of cobalt amino-methyl sulfonate is shown in Fig. 4–3.

A chelating group may exist as several forms of an uncharged molecule, but in the presence of a metal ion, it is stabilized into a single form. For instance, acetylacetone has the following equilibrium:

$$\underset{\text{Ketone}}{CH_3—\underset{\underset{O}{\|}}{C}—CH_2—\underset{\underset{O}{\|}}{C}—CH_3} \rightleftharpoons \underset{\text{Enol}}{CH_3—\underset{\underset{OH}{|}}{C}=CH—\underset{\underset{O}{\|}}{C}—CH_3}$$

The enolic hydrogen is acidic and is replaceable with metal ions. In chromium solutions chromium (III) acetylacetonate is formed whose structure is shown in Figure 4–4. Many of these compounds are very stable. For example, the corresponding beryllium compound boils at 270°C without decomposition.

Other groups in organic molecules can act as either acidic or electron-donating groups. An example is —N—OH, where the hydrogen may be removed or the nitrogen pair of electrons may be used. For the beginning chemist, the most familiar compound of this type is the dimethylglyoxime derivative of nickel.

Other possible ligands are tridentate, quadradentate, and even hexadentate. The ethylenediaminetetraacetate ion encages the metal ion to form a six-coordinated structure (Fig. 4–5). Even metals such as Mg^{2+} and Ca^{2+}, which ordinarily do not form stable coordination compounds, react with EDTA.

ISOMERIZATION

The possibility of stereoisomerization has been discussed for the case of a molecule of the type MA_4X_2, where A and X are different ligands. In addition to this example, there are numerous other types of isomerization which are found.

1. Optical isomerism. If a molecule of $Co(en)_2Cl_2^+$ (en is an abbreviation for ethylenediamine) is prepared, several structures are possible (Fig. 4–6).

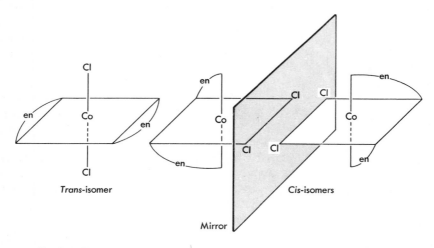

Fig. 4–6. The three possible isomers of dichloro *bis* (ethylenediamine) cobalt (III) ion.

The relationship between the two *cis* forms is simply that of a right and left hand, i.e. mirror images. This effect is known as optical isomerism because each isomer rotates plane-polarized light in opposite directions. It always occurs when there is no plane of symmetry in the molecule.

The optical rotary power in these inorganic complexes is usually much larger than for organic substances. Figure 4–7 shows the specific rotation as a function of wavelength for $l-Co(en)_2Cl_2^+$.

2. Ionization isomerism. It is possible to interchange a ligand and an ion in a salt of a coordination compound. This is called ionization isomerism. Thus $[Co(NH_3)_4ClI]I$ has the same empirical formula as $[Co(NH_3)I_2]Cl$, but is a different chemical.

3. Coordination isomerism. A salt consisting of a complex anion and a complex cation may be prepared. In such a case, the ligands may be interchanged to give different isomers. Examples are $[Co(NH_3)_6][Cr(C_2O_4)_3]$ and $[Cr(NH_3)_6][Co(C_2O_4)_3]$.

4. Polymerization isomerism. $Pt(NH_3)_2Cl_2$ and $[Pt(NH_3)_4][PtCl_4]$ have the same empirical formula but obviously have different structures. $[Pt(NH_3)_3Cl]_2$ $[PtCl_4]$ also has the same empirical formula. Such isomerism is called "polymerization" isomerism, which it is noted, is not the usual usage of the term polymerization.

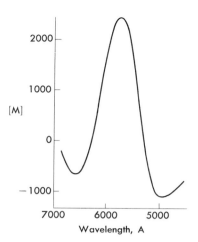

Fig. 4–7. The specific optical rotation of light by $l-Co(en)_2Cl_2^+$ as a function of wavelength.

5. Linkage isomerism. Ligands such as NO_2^- may be attached to the central metal ion through either the oxygen or the nitrogen. Two separable compounds are formed which generally have different colors. Examples are

$$[(NH_3)_5Cr\text{—}ONO]^{2+}$$

and

$$[(NH_3)_5CrNO_2]^{2+}.$$

6. Coordination position isomerism. Bridged complexes may be prepared in which there are two central metal ions which share a ligand or set of ligands. In such a compound, the remaining ligands may be interchanged to form several isomers. An example is illustrated in Fig. 4–8.

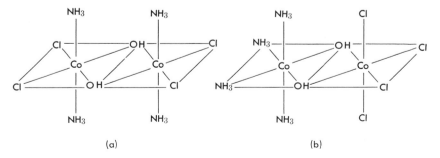

(a)   (b)

Fig. 4–8. Two coordination position isomers of a dicobalt compound.

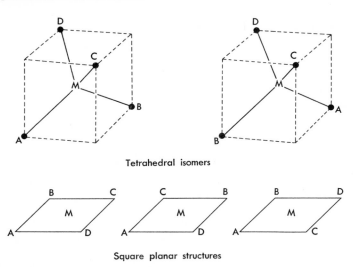

Tetrahedral isomers

Square planar structures

Fig. 4–9. The isomeric structures of tetrahedral and square planar compounds of the formula MABCD.

COORDINATION WITH SYMMETRIES OTHER THAN OCTAHEDRAL

Although coordination with six groups is very common, other coordination numbers are also possible. The coordination of a metal ion by four ligands occurs very frequently and should be familiar in such compounds as MnO_4^-, $Zn(NH_3)_4^{2+}$, $PtCl_4^{2-}$, and $PbCl_4^{2-}$.

There are two possible symmetric arrangements of four ligands about a metal ion. Either the ligands form a square with the metal ion in the center or else they are arranged at the corners of a tetrahedron. Chemically it is possible to distinguish between these cases for the compound type MABCD. If the material is square planar, three structural isomers are possible. If the compound is tetrahedral, only optical isomers are possible. Figure 4–9 shows the different isomers.

Structures which have two ligands are also rather common. Examples are $Ag(NH_3)_2^+$ and $Hg(NH_3)_2^{2+}$. Compounds with coordination numbers of three, five, seven, eight, and nine occur but are less common than those discussed above. Coordination not usually found for a given ion may be forced by placing an ion in a host crystal of the proper symmetry. This trick has been used to study ions in varying symmetries.

CRYSTAL FIELD THEORY

In Chapter 3, it was shown that a metal ion with nonzero orbital angular momentum in an electric field has some of the degeneracy of its energy levels removed. The spectral properties of the ion are changed accordingly, and information may be obtained about the levels from examination of the spectrum.

In a coordination compound or for an ion in a crystal lattice, an electric field is produced at the ion site by the surrounding ligands or ions. Even if the ion is surrounded by neutral molecules such as water, the ion will experience an electric field due to the electric dipole moments of the molecules. It is the purpose of this section to develop, using symmetry arguments, the effect such an electric field has on a given ion and to show how spectral information gives structural information about the complex.

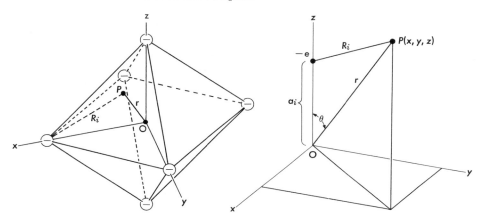

Fig. 4–10. A diagram of a point located within an octahedron of unit charges.

Fig. 4–11. The coordinates of a point P relative to a point charge on the z-axis.

THE ELECTRIC FIELD

The analysis of an electric field may be started by replacing all the ions to be considered by point charges. Such an approximation was used in Chapter 1 to calculate bond energies, etc., for ionic crystals. The subsequent analysis is therefore called an ionic or crystal-field model.

Consider a positive metal ion surrounded by six negative ions or point charges. The point charges are arranged at the corners of a regular octahedron at a distance a_i from the metal ion at the center. There will be an electrostatic attraction which may be described by a potential of the form

$$V = \sum_i \frac{Z_1 Z_2 e^2}{a_i},$$

$$(4-1)$$

which is the potential at the metal ion nucleus due to the surrounding charges. But the situation we need to consider is the force that an electron experiences in the space between the origin and the negative point charges. Figure 4–10 illustrates the situation for a point P inside the octahedron. The potential energy is now given by

$$V = \sum_i \frac{Z_1 Z_2 e^2}{R_i},$$

$$(4-2)$$

where R_i is the distance from P to the ligands. Although Eq. (4–2) is similar in appearance to Eq. (4–1), it has the difficulty that R_i depends not only on the position of the ligands but also on the coordinates of the point P.

We may clarify the nature of the distance R_i by considering the potential at P arising from only a single point charge on the z-axis, as shown in Fig. 4–11. Let us call the distance from P to the origin the radius vector $\mathbf{r}$. From the diagram it is easy to see that

$$\mathbf{R}_i = \mathbf{r} - \mathbf{a}_i \tag{4–3}$$

or that

$$R_i^2 = r^2 + a_i^2 - 2ra_i \cos \theta. \tag{4–4}$$

Upon substitution into Eq. (4–2), we have

$$V = \frac{Z_1 Z_2 e^2}{(r^2 + a_i^2 - 2ra_i \cos \theta)^{1/2}}, \tag{4–5}$$

where $r^2 = x^2 + y^2 + z^2$. If the magnitude of $\mathbf{r}$ is less than $\mathbf{a}$, the denominator of Eq. (4–5) may be rewritten as

$$(a_i^2 + r^2 - 2ra_i \cos \theta)^{-1/2} = a_i^{-1}[1 + r^2/a_i^2 - 2(r/a_i) \cos \theta]^{-1/2} \tag{4–6}$$

$$= a_i^{-1}(1 + x)^{-1/2}, \tag{4–7}$$

where $x = r^2/a_i^2 - 2(r/a_i) \cos \theta$. The function x is a function of the coordinates of P but is always less than unity. Therefore, we may expand Eq. (4–7) with the binomial series to obtain

$$V = \frac{Z_1 Z_2 e^2}{a_i} \left(1 - \frac{1}{2} x + \frac{3}{8} x^2 - \frac{15}{48} x^3 + \cdots \right). \tag{4–8}$$

For the general potential energy of Eq. (4–2), a similar expression is obtained which differs in that a summation over the ligands is performed.

At this point in the calculation, we could substitute the expression for x in terms of x, y, and z to obtain the potential form desired. However, before we carry out the calculation in detail, what can be learned from the symmetry of the potential? The regular octahedron belongs to the class of objects which has the symmetry of a cube. The potential energy must have the same value at point P whether or not we change the octahedron of charges by a cubic symmetry operation. This statement is usually phrased as "the potential energy must be invariant under the symmetry operations of the cube."

In Chapter 1 it was shown that for a cube there are 48 symmetry operations which may be expressed as the transformation properties of x, y, and z. If our potential is to be invariant, then the transformations of x, y, and z must not change the form of the potential. If a term in the expansion is not invariant, then it cannot be contained in the cubic-field potential energy. Therefore, we need only examine the 48 symmetry operations to find the terms in Eq. (4–8) which do not change.

Fortunately, a simplification is possible because the symmetry operations may be classified according to the type or class of operation. This may be seen, because a rotation by $\pm\pi/2$ about the z-axis is very much like a rotation about the x-axis by $\pm\pi/2$. Thus, any one of this class of operations generally gives all the information necessary. There are six rotations by $\pm\pi/2$ about the principal axes. Further classifications are possible. For example, the inversion operation, $x \to -x$, $y \to -y$, $z \to -z$, is in a class by itself, because there is no other operation like it. Since half of the 48 operations result from a symmetry operation followed by inversion, we need only consider 24 and the inversion.

Let us consider the operation of rotation by π about the x-axis followed by inversion. This sequence of operations causes the transformation

$$\begin{array}{ccc}
\text{Rotation by} & & \text{Inversion} \\
\pi \text{ about } x & & \\
x \longrightarrow & x \longrightarrow & -x \\
y \longrightarrow & -y \longrightarrow & y \\
z \longrightarrow & -z \longrightarrow & z
\end{array}$$

It may be recalled that a rotation followed by an inversion is a reflection. In this case the operation is a reflection in the yz-plane which must leave the potential invariant, that is, $V(x, y, z) = V(-x, y, z)$. Therefore, only even powers of x need be considered. In a similar manner, odd powers of z and y are excluded.

Zeroth-order terms in x, y, or z have only spherical symmetry, and we defer discussion of them for a while. The second-order terms must have the form

$$C_1(x^2) + C_2(y^2) + C_3(z^2) + C_4(xy) + C_5(xz) + C_6(yz), \tag{4-9}$$

where the C_i are constants which depend on a_i and the ligand charges. Consider this time a rotation about z by $\pi/2$. This operation does not leave Eq. (4-9) invariant unless $C_1 = C_2$, $C_4 = -C_4$, $C_5 = -C_6$, and $C_5 = C_6$. The only solution possible is $C_4 = C_5 = C_6 = 0$. Similarly, it may be shown that if a rotation about y by $\pi/2$ is considered, then $C_3 = C_1$. Therefore, the only contribution to the potential energy from second-order terms is

$$C_1(x^2 + y^2 + z^2) = C_1 r^2, \tag{4-10}$$

which is again a spherical function.

The next-order terms to consider are fourth order. By reasoning similar to that for the squared term, the fourth-order term must be

$$A(x^4 + y^4 + z^4), \tag{4-11}$$

which does not have spherical but only cubic symmetry.

Higher-order terms such as $x^2 y^2 z^2$ are also invariant under the operations of the cubic group. Although it is outside the scope of this book, it may be shown that for ions with d-electrons in their ground-state configuration, terms higher than fourth order need not be considered. Our final potential-energy expression for a cubic electrostatic field is, therefore,

$$V(x, y, z) = \text{Terms in } \frac{1}{a_i} + \text{Terms in } \frac{r^2}{a_i^3} + A(x^4 + y^4 + z^4). \quad (4\text{--}12)$$

This problem has illustrated how simple symmetry arguments may be used to calculate the form of a potential energy expression. The calculation could have been done explicitly by inserting the coordinates of the ligands into Eq. (4–8), but this is a tedious job. However, it must be carried out to give the value of the constant A in Eq. (4–12). For an octahedral distribution of six point charges, it is found that

$$A = \frac{35}{4} \frac{Z_1 Z_2 e^2}{a_i^5}. \quad (4\text{--}13)$$

For 8-fold coordinated compounds, the value of A is $-(70/9)(Z_1 Z_2 e^2/a_i^5)$, and for a tetrahedral arrangement of four charges, the coefficient is $-(35/9)(Z_1 Z_2 e^2/a_i^5)$.

The value of the parameter A is important for our understanding, because it shows that the potential energy reverses sign if the configuration of point charges changes from octahedral to 8-fold coordination or tetrahedral coordination. It may be anticipated that the splitting of the energy levels of an ion will be quite different in these three cubic-field cases.

NONCUBIC-FIELD POTENTIALS

If an octahedral charge arrangement is distorted so that the charges on the z-axis are at a distance greater than a_i, then a change occurs in the form of the potential energy. Again, symmetry arguments may be used. Figure 4–12 shows that in this case, there is no longer a 3-fold symmetry about a $(1, 1, 1)$ axis, nor is there 4-fold symmetry about the x- and y-axes. Thus, we cannot use the operations $x \to y$, $y \to z$, $z \to x$, or $x \to z$, $z \to -x$, etc. Terms involving x^2, y^2, and z^2 must remain. Consider a general second-order term of the form $V = C_1 x^2 + C_2 y^2 + C_3 z^2$. A rotation about z by $\pi/2$ changes $x \to y$, $y \to -x$, and $z \to z$; V becomes $C_1 y^2 + C_2 x^2 + C_3 z^2$, which, if it is to be invariant, can only be true if $C_1 = C_2$. There are no symmetry operations

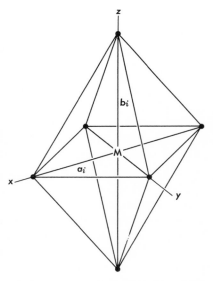

Fig. 4–12. The distorted octahedron resulting from a lengthening of the distances to the point charges on the z-axis.

which change z into either x or y. Thus our potential has a second-order term,

$$V = C_2(x^2 + y^2) + C_3 z^2. \qquad (4\text{--}14)$$

Equation (4–13) is added to Eq. (4–1) to give a complete expression for tetragonal fields. If the xy-plane is also distorted, then $C_1 \neq C_2 \neq C_3$ for the second-order potential.

THE SPLITTING OF ENERGY LEVELS OF IONS IN COMPLEXES

To obtain a general idea of how a crystal-field potential affects the energy levels of a free ion, let us consider as an example Ti^{3+} in an octahedral field. Ti^{3+} has a single $3d$-electron with an argon core. The ground state is a ^2D. The energy levels are found by solving Schroedinger's equation, where the Hamiltonian includes all the electron-electron and electron-proton interactions. We call this Hamiltonian the free-ion Hamiltonian.

The presence of an octahedral distribution of charges about the Ti^{3+} ion has the effect of adding to the free-ion Hamiltonian the potential energy of Eq. (4–12). The total Hamiltonian to be used in Schroedinger's equation is now

$$\mathcal{H} = \mathcal{H}_{\text{free ion}} + V_{\text{cubic}}. \qquad (4\text{--}15)$$

The addition of V_{cubic} affects the energy, because it is a function of both the radius and the angles, θ and φ. The radial wave functions for d-electrons are identical so that the radial part of Eq. (4–15) shifts all energy levels by the same amount.

Let us, therefore, confine our attention to the angular wave functions belonging to a single d-electron. We saw in Chapter 3 that a convenient set is

$$x^2 - y^2, \quad 3z^2 - r^2, \quad xy, \quad yz, \quad zx.$$

We can calculate the effect of V_{cubic} on this set if we note that the wave functions used to describe a system must have the same symmetry as the system. Thus the Ti^{3+} complex must have wave functions with cubic symmetry. We ask, therefore, that the above functions, or some linear combination of them, transform properly under the cubic operation. This problem was previously considered in Chapter 1, Problem 4, where it was shown that $x^2 - y^2$ and $3z^2 - r^2$ transform only among themselves and that xy, yz, and zx transform among themselves. The effect of V_{cubic} is to remove the equivalence of $x^2 - y^2$ and $3z^2 - r^2$ from xy, yz, and zx. Since they are no longer degenerate, the 5-fold degenerate energy level of the free ion is split into two levels, one which is 2-fold and the other which is 3-fold degenerate. The energy-level diagram is shown schematically in Fig. 4–13.

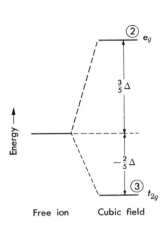

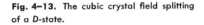

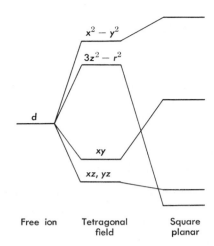

Fig. 4–13. The cubic crystal field splitting of a D-state.

Fig. 4–14. The crystal field splitting of a D-state in a tetragonal and square planar field.

The custom is to call $x^2 - y^2$ and $3z^2 - r^2$ the e_g- or d_γ-orbitals, and xy, xz, and yz the t_{2g}- or d_ϵ-orbitals. The energy difference will be called Δ, although it is frequently called $10Dq$, where $Dq = A$ in the potential energy equation (4–13).

Another more pictorial method of obtaining the same conclusion is to observe that electrons in orbits which point toward high electron density must have more energy than those electrons in orbits which avoid negative charges. For an octahedral charge distribution, the electron will preferentially be in the t_{2g}-orbitals if the ion is to be in its ground state. The electron will require more energy in an amount of Δ if it is to be in the e_g-orbitals.

If Ti^{3+} is placed in an 8-fold coordination complex, the energy level diagram is inverted, because the sign of A in the potential energy is reversed. A tetrahedral field will also invert the energy diagram, and the splitting should be approximately half the octahedral and 8-fold cases, because

$$A_{\text{octahedral}} \approx -A_{\text{8-fold}} \approx -\tfrac{1}{2}A_{\text{tetrahedral}}.$$

A distortion of the octahedral charge distribution by moving the charges on the z-axis away from the origin will produce a potential given by Eq. (4–14). The xy-orbital no longer belongs in the set with xz or yz, and $3z^2 - r^2$ is separated from $x^2 - y^2$. Four energy levels are obtained which are derived from the octahedral case, as shown in Fig. 4–13. It should be noted that a square planar configuration of negative charges will have the same number of energy levels as the distorted octahedron, but the displacements will be quite different. The $3z^2 - r^2$ orbital should have a low energy relative to even the yz- or xz-orbitals (Fig. 4-14).

MANY-ELECTRON PROBLEM

The calculation of the energy levels for ions with more than one d-electron requires further theoretical consideration beyond the present scope of this book. We can, however, outline the calculation which will be useful in discussing actual experimental results on chemical compounds.

It is convenient to distinguish between two cases; the *medium*-field case and the *strong*-field case. The medium-field case corresponds to the consideration of an ion in an electrostatic field which is but a small perturbation upon the free ion. It was shown in Chapter 3 that the ground state of an ion with a d^n-configuration has the same symmetry properties as an S-state if n is 0, 5, 10; a D-state if n is 1, 4, 6, 9; or an F-state if n is 2, 3, 7 or 8. An S-state cannot be split by an external electrostatic field, because it has spherical symmetry. Therefore, we expect no electric field splittings for Sc^{3+}, Mn^{2+}, or Zn^{2+} in the medium-field case. The ground-state energy of an ion with a D-state will be split as shown in Fig. 4–13. The splitting of an F-state by a cubic field is more complicated, but again by symmetry arguments it is possible to show that it splits into three levels. Two of them are 3-fold degenerate, and one is nondegenerate, as shown in Fig. 4–15.

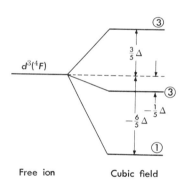

We could also obtain approximately the same energy level diagram by filling up the t_{2g}- and e_g-orbitals with the restriction that the spin angular momentum is a maximum. Thus the octahedral field configurations for a d^n-ion are $t_{2g}^{n-m}e_g^m$. For example, the ground-state configuration for Mn^{3+} is $3d^4$, which in an octahedral field is $t_{2g}^3e_g^1$. Mn^{2+} with five $3d$-electrons has the octahedral field configuration $t_{2g}^3e_g^2$. Since all levels are filled with electrons having the same spin angular momentum, any further additions must cause spin pairing.

Fig. 4–15. The cubic crystal field splitting of an F-state.

Up to now there has been no discussion of the order of the levels except that for a single d-electron, where the t_{2g}-orbitals are lowest. Consider the case of copper (II) in which the ground-state configuration is d^9. All the orbitals are filled with electrons except one. An alternative method of dealing with the d^9-configuration is to consider it as a single positive d-hole. That is, any transition of an electron from one orbital to another may be considered as a positive hole leaving behind an electron in a formerly vacant orbital and annihilating an electron in a formerly filled orbital. Therefore, the energy-level diagram of a d^9-configuration in an octahedral field must be inverted from a d^1-configuration. This rule holds true for all complimentary configurations so that d^n has the same energy level diagram as d^{10-n} except for inversion of the order of the levels.

TABLE 4–1

Ion configuration	Ion ground state	Complexed ion configuration	Medium-field energy level diagram
d^1	^2D	t_{2g}	A
d^2	^3F	t_{2g}^2	B
d^3	^4F	t_{2g}^3	Inverted B
d^4	^5D	$t_{2g}^3 e_g$	Inverted A
d^5	^6S	$t_{2g}^3 e_g^2$	No splitting
d^6	^5D	$t_{2g}^4 e_g^2$	A
d^7	^4F	$t_{2g}^5 e_g^2$	B
d^8	^3F	$t_{2g}^6 e_g^2$	Inverted B
d^9	^2D	$t_{2g}^6 e_g^3$	Inverted A
d^{10}	^1S	$t_{2g}^6 e_g^4$	No splitting

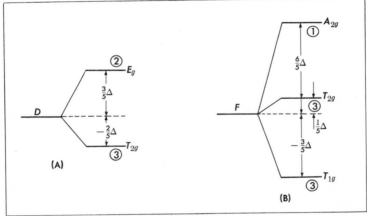

A similar relationship of levels occurs between the d^1- and d^4-configurations because the d^4-configuration may be thought of as a d^5-configuration plus a d-positive hole. The d^4-energy level diagram is therefore inverted from the d^1-diagram. In Table 4–1, the medium-field energy level diagrams are shown for all d^n-configurations. Tetrahedral or 8-fold coordination reverses the order of the energy levels.

The strong field case is simpler to deal with in many ways. The electrostatic external field is assumed to be sufficient to overcome the coupling energy of the electron spins. In other words, the e_g-orbitals have such a high energy that they are not populated because Hund's rules break down, and spin pairing occurs. Therefore, the t_{2g}-orbitals are filled completely with six electrons before the e_g-orbitals are filled. The electron configurations are given in Table 4–2. We have also listed in Table 4–2 the energy of stabilization for each ion configuration.

TABLE 4–2

Ion electron configuration	Complexed ion configuration	Energy of stabilization
d^1	t_{2g}^1	$-\frac{2}{5}\Delta$
d^2	t_{2g}^2	$-\frac{4}{5}\Delta$
d^3	t_{2g}^3	$-\frac{6}{5}\Delta$
d^4	t_{2g}^4	$-\frac{8}{5}\Delta$
d^5	t_{2g}^5	-2Δ
d^6	t_{2g}^6	$-\frac{12}{5}\Delta$
d^7	$t_{2g}^6 e_g^1$	$-\frac{9}{5}\Delta$
d^8	$t_{2g}^6 e_g^2$	$-\frac{6}{5}\Delta$
d^9	$t_{2g}^6 e_g^3$	$-\frac{3}{5}\Delta$
d^{10}	$t_{2g}^6 e_g^4$	0

This energy is the difference between the sum of the electron energies with and without the cubic fourth-order potential. Thus the energy difference for a single d-electron is $-\frac{2}{5}\Delta$ and that for two d-electrons is $2(-\frac{2}{5}\Delta) = -\frac{4}{5}\Delta$, because each electron is in a t_{2g}-orbital. The maximum stabilization energy occurs for d^6 because additional electrons will go into the e_g-orbital, which gives a positive energy contribution. The general formula for a $t_{2g}^{n-m}e_g^m$ configuration is

$$E_{\text{stab}} = -(n-m)\frac{2}{5}\Delta + m\frac{3}{5}\Delta. \tag{4-16}$$

The determination of Δ. Let us now determine the value of the parameter Δ. From our discussion of the potential energy we can see that Δ depends on:

(1) The interionic spacing a_i between the metal ion and ligand to the fifth power.

(2) The charge on the metal ion and the ligand.

(3) The radius r at which the potential is evaluated. Quantum-mechanically, this is expressed as the average value of the fourth power of the radius. The actual value of this quantity depends upon the particular radial wave function. For $3d$-electrons the Δ-parameter should be less than for $4d$-electrons because of the greater spatial extent of the $4d$ wave function.

The calculation of Δ from first principles is difficult and generally unsatisfactory. However, Δ may be obtained from optical absorption spectra of ions in octahedral or near octahedral coordination. The observed absorptions which account for the colors of transition metal ions result from an excitation of the type

$$t_{2g}^{n-m}e_g^m \rightarrow t_{2g}^{n-(m+1)}e_g^{m+1}. \tag{4-17}$$

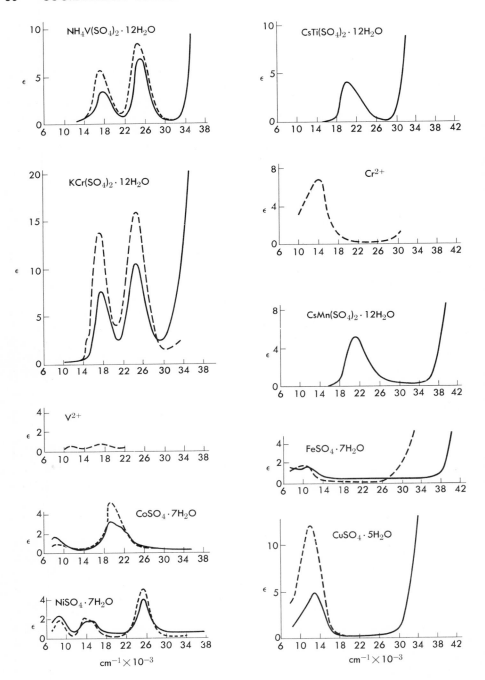

Fig. 4–16. The optical spectra of the hydrated 3d-transition metal ions. [O. G. Holmes and D. S. McClure, *J. Chem. Phys.* **26**, 1686 (1957).] Broken lines are aqueous solution spectra; solid lines are crystal spectra.

Figure 4–16 shows the absorption spectra of several hydrated $3d$-transition metal ions in water solutions and crystals. In Fig. 4–17, the spectra of Ni^{2+} in water, concentrated HCl, NH_3, and CN^- solutions are given.

The calculation of Δ for ions for which the D-state is the lowest state is very simple. From Fig. 4–16, we see that only one rather broad absorption peak is observed for Ti^{3+}, Cr^{2+}, Mn^{3+}, Fe^{2+}, and Cu^{2+}. This result is in accord with our predictions that a D-state is split into only two levels. The value of Δ is just the energy at the maximum of the absorption. For the 2+ ions Δ is about 10,000 cm^{-1}, whereas for the 3+ ions Δ is approximately 20,000 cm^{-1}. This variation of Δ with metal ion charge is also in accord with our prediction above.

The calculation of Δ for ions with F ground states is only slightly more difficult. As an example consider the case of Ni^{2+}, which has a d^8 ground-state configuration. Let us assume that this is a medium-field case so that to a first approximation the energy levels arise from a ^3F Hund ground state. The reason for choosing a medium field is that the second and third contributions to Δ enumerated above are less than for higher charged ions or for $4d$- and $5d$-ions. Since a ^3F-state splits in an octahedral field as shown in Table 4–1, we should observe two transitions, one with an energy of Δ and the other of $\frac{9}{5}\Delta$.

The spectrum of $Ni(H_2O)_6^{2+}$ shows a peak absorption at an energy of 8500 cm^{-1}, another at 14,000 cm^{-1}, a much more intense peak at 26,000 cm^{-1}, and an extremely intense peak at about 40,000 cm^{-1}. Let us assume that the lowest energy is the transition from the ground to the first excited state. The value of Δ is therefore 8500 cm^{-1}, and we predict that another line should occur at $\frac{9}{5}\Delta$ or 15,300 cm^{-1}. This value is not too far from the observed levels at 14,000 cm^{-1}.

We are left with two lines to explain. The very intense band at 40,000 cm^{-1} is called a charge transfer band. Because the intensity is many times greater than the intensities of the lines we considered above, the transitions between levels must be quite unlike transitions between d-levels. We will therefore not consider them further, although they are very interesting in terms of the understanding of a complex as a whole.

The absorption at 26,000 cm^{-1} is in many respects similar to the other less intense peaks. In fact it arises from a transition from the lowest energy level to a level which originates from a different Hund state, namely the ^3P-state. When the interaction of higher Hund states with the ground states is considered, the calculated absorptions occur at 8500 cm^{-1}, 14,000 cm^{-1}, and 27,000 cm^{-1}, which agrees very well with the measured values.

The general problem of the interaction of higher states with the ground state has been considered by numerous people. Figure 4–18 shows several graphs of the results of such calculations for different ions. These so-called "Orgel diagrams" are a plot of energy as a function of Δ for Hund states arising from a single electron configuration. The diagram for Ni^{2+} in Fig. 4–18 may be used to calculate Δ for the other complexes whose spectra are given in Fig. 4–17. For $Ni(NH_3)_6^{2+}$ the spectrum is shifted to shorter wave lengths, which results

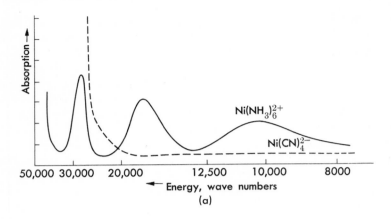

(a)

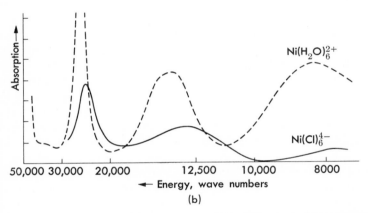

(b)

Fig. 4-17. The optical absorption spectra of $Ni(H_2O)_6^{2+}$, $NiCl_6^{4-}$, $Ni(NH_3)_6^{2+}$, and $Ni(CN)_4^{2-}$.

in a value of $10,600$ cm^{-1} for Δ. In contrast, the spectrum of Ni^{2+} in HCl is shifted to longer wave lengths corresponding to a Δ of 7300 cm^{-1}.

From the analysis of several nickel coordination compound spectra, it is found that the order of increasing Δ for various ligands is as follows:

Ligand	Δ in cm^{-1}
bromide	7,000
chloride	7,300
H_2O	8,500
NH_3	10,600
en	11,200
o-phenantholine	12,700

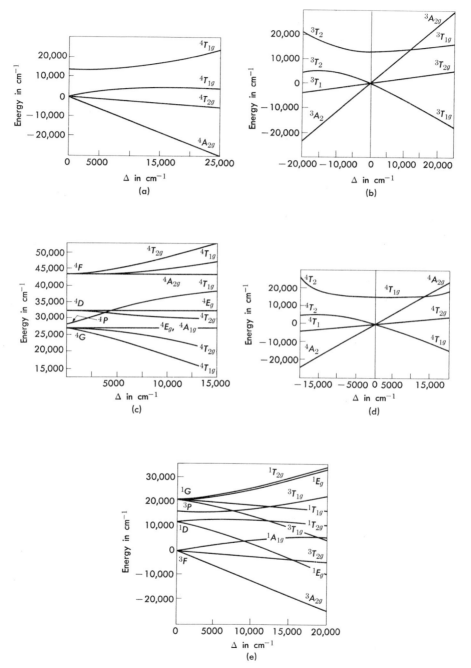

Fig. 4-18. Orgel diagrams; the energy-level diagrams for (a) Cr^{3+}, (b) V^{2+}, (c) Mn^{2+}, (d) Co^{2+}, (e) Ni^{2+}. [L. Orgel, *J. Chem. Phys.* **23**, 1004 (1955).]

From the spectra of several different metal ions it is found that a general order of increasing Δ is the same as the order of the following ligands:

$$I^-, \; Br^-, \; Cl^-, \; F^-, \; CH_3CH_2OH, \; H_2O, \; NH_3, \; en, \; NO_2, \; CN^-,$$

which is called the Fajans-Tsuchida spectrochemical series.

In Fig. 4–17, a spectrum of the yellow nickel cyanide complex is also shown. There is no similarity between this spectrum and those of the other nickel compounds, which indicates that the complex in solution does not have octahedral symmetry, a fact which we might suspect from the formula $Ni(CN)_4^{2-}$.

Measurements of electrostatic splitting in strong octahedral fields are hampered by other effects which appear. For instance, $Ni(CN)_6^{4-}$ does not form because the arrangement of four CN^- gives a lower total energy for the complex. However, there are various compounds suited for examination, among which are hexafluorides of the 4d- and 5d-ions. The simplest spectrum is that of ReF_6, which is shown in Fig. 4–19. The electronic ground state of Re^{6+} is $5d^1$. The octahedral splitting should give rise to one line. The spectrum in Fig. 4–19 is, however, more complicated. A correct analysis shows that the low energy peak results from a splitting of the t_{2g}-orbital due to interaction of the electron spin angular momentum with the orbital angular momentum. The absorption lines near 32,500 cm^{-1} are approximately the value of the crystal field splitting due to the strong field. Another strong-field example is the spectrum of the crystal K_2ReCl_6, in which the Re^{4+} ion has the configuration $5d^3$. An analysis leads to an energy difference between the t_{2g}- and e_g-orbitals of 33,500 cm^{-1}. In general, the values of Δ for 4d- and 5d-ions range from 25,000 to 35,000 cm^{-1}.

The experimental values of Δ for the various cases may be summarized as follows:

Medium-field case:	M^{2+}	10,000 cm^{-1}
	M^{3+}	20,000 cm^{-1}
Strong-field case:		30,000 cm^{-1}

However, caution should be observed in using these numbers indiscriminately.

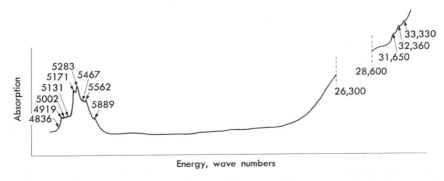

Fig. 4–19. The spectrum of ReF$_6$. [Moffitt, Goodman, Fred, and Weinstock, *Mol. Phys* **2,** 109 (1959).]

LINE WIDTH

The spectra shown in Figs. 4–16, 4–17 and 4–19 have a characteristic which is almost always observed. The lines associated with the crystal-field transition or, as it is frequently called, the d-d transitions are rather broad. Sometimes lines are observed which are very sharp in contrast. Such a case is observed for MnF_2, which is shown in Fig. 4–20. The lines at 25,000 cm^{-1} are much sharper than the others.

The reason for the difference may be explained as follows: the central ion is not surrounded by fixed ligands, but there are motions of the ions relative to each other. Since Δ depends upon the internuclear distance, a_i, a range of values of energy are allowed for a given transition. However, in some cases the variation of the ground state and an excited state as a function of Δ may be exactly the same. Therefore the energy difference is independent of Δ, and the line will be narrow. In the case of Mn^{2+}, the Orgel diagram shows that one level from the ^4G-, as well as ^4D- and ^4F-states, is independent of Δ. Since the ground state, ^6S, is not split by a crystal field, the lines corresponding to transitions among these levels will be sharp.

NONOCTAHEDRAL COORDINATION

An octahedral electric field has high symmetry or, in other words, it has a large number of symmetry operations. As a consequence, we have seen that the orbital degeneracy of a transition metal ion is only partially removed. Consider the case of Cr^{2+}, which has a d^4-ion configuration. In an octahedral field the ^5D ground state is split into a lower doubly degenerate orbital level

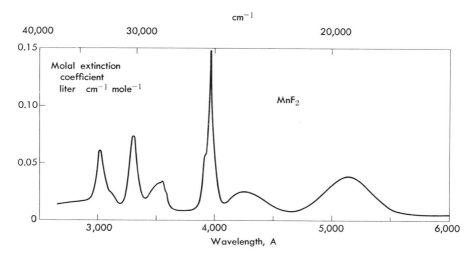

Fig. 4–20. The absorption spectrum of a single crystal of MnF2 at 25°C. The optical path was the C-axis of the crystal. [J. W. Stout, *J. Chem. Phys.* **33**, 709 (1959).]

and a higher triplet with an energy of separation of about $10,000 \text{ cm}^{-1}$. The complex ion configuration is $t_{2g}^3 e_g^1$ for the medium-field case. Thus, the xy-, yz-, and xz-orbitals are each occupied by an electron, and either the $x^2 - y^2$ or $3z^2 - r^2$ orbital is occupied by the remaining electron. Let us consider that the electron is in the $3z^2 - r^2$ orbital. The ligands on the z-axis will have a repulsive interaction with this electron and will tend to minimize this by moving out. In a similar manner, the ligands in the xy-plane experience no such repulsion and are attracted by the positive metal ion. We might expect that Cr^{2+} compounds will never have truly octahedral symmetry but will have a distorted arrangement of ligands with four short bonds and two long bonds. This distortion is observed for a number of Cr^{2+} compounds. For example, in a crystal of CrF_2, the Cr^{2+} is surrounded by an octahedron of fluoride ions arranged with two at 2.43 A, and four at 2.00 A. As we might expect, cupric fluoride has a similar distortion with two F^- at 2.27 A and four F^- at 1.93 A. Of course, there is the equal possibility that the odd electron would be in the $x^2 - y^2$ orbital, in which case four long bonds and two short bonds would result. A more detailed analysis is necessary to predict which distortion will actually occur.

The energy level diagram of Cr^{2+} in a distorted octahedral environment will differ from the cubic case. No longer are the $3z^2 - r^2$ and $x^2 - y^2$ orbitals degenerate, and even the xy-orbital is split off from the xz- and yz-orbitals. For Cr^{2+} the splitting is shown in Fig. 4–21. The actual ground-state splittings are relatively small and are generally not observed by optical spectroscopy. Figure 4–21 does illustrate that the energy of the ground state is lowered by the distortion. We may therefore expect to have a distorted octahedron whenever the ground-state energy can be lowered by a small displacement of the ligands. This will occur for all octahedral ground states which have orbital degeneracy. Thus, d^1, d^2, d^4, d^6, d^7, and d^9 ion configurations will

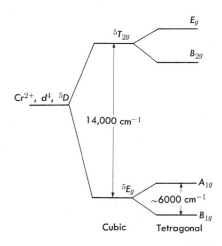

Fig. 4–21. The energy-level diagram of Cr^{2+} in a tetragonal crystal field.

generally form distorted complexes. The other configuration ions have singlet orbital ground states which are not affected by any small movement of the ligands. This effect was first postulated by Jahn and Teller.

Is it possible to predict the amount of distortion? At present the answer is negative, but we can make some qualitative observations. Let us compare Fe^{2+} and Cr^{2+}. Both have ^5D-states for the ion ground state which arise from d^6- and d^4-configurations, respectively. In an octahedral field, Fe^{2+} will have the configuration $t_{2g}^4 e_g^2$, whereas Cr^{2+} will have $t_{2g}^3 e_g^1$. These configurations are to be compared with Mn^{2+}, an S-state ion, whose octahedral configuration is

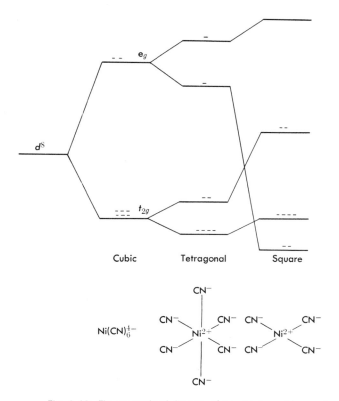

Fig. 4–22. The energy-level diagram of the nickel cyanide complex.

$t_{2g}^3 e_g^2$. The ferrous ion may be thought of as an ion whose spherical symmetry is destroyed by the extra electron in a t_{2g}-orbital. A t_{2g}-electron does not interact very strongly with the ligands; thus the Jahn-Teller distortion is not large. For Cr^{2+} the spherical symmetry is lost because of the absence of an electron in the e_g-orbital. Any small displacement of the ligands will have a large effect on the motion of the single e_g-electron. Therefore, it is expected that Cr^{2+} ions will show larger Jahn-Teller distortions than Fe^{2+} ions. Several magnetic experiments support this argument. Similar arguments apply also to Cu^{2+} ions.

In the strong-field case, the ideas presented above may be used to show that ions with the configurations t_{2g}^3 and t_{2g}^6 will not show Jahn-Teller effects. For d^n-ions with $n > 6$, strong distortion effects do occur. Let us reexamine the $Ni(CN)_4^{2-}$ molecule. Ni^{2+} has a d^8-configuration, and CN^- has the strongest ligand field effect. If a regular octahedral arrangement were maintained to form the compound $Ni(CN)_6^{4-}$, the electrons would be distributed as $t_{2g}^6 e_g^2$. But this arrangement forces a large electrostatic repulsion between the e_g-electrons and the CN^-. The CN^- along the z-axis will move out, as shown in Fig. 4–22, to minimize the energy. The result is that the d-electrons redistribute themselves among the energy levels so that the most stable configuration occurs with the CN^- on the z-axis completely removed. The d-electrons are distributed among the xy, yz, xz, and $3z^2 - r^2$ orbitals in pairs.

The example of $Ni(CN)_4^{2-}$ serves to illustrate that in strong fields, distorted complexes are always observed for ions with more than six d-electrons. Because the $4d$- and $5d$-ions generally have a high oxidation state and have a large spatial radial wave function, they are always included in the strong-field case.

If the energy can be decreased by a distortion and eventually by the removal of two ions, then cannot the removal of more ions reduce the symmetry further and thus decrease the energy? In general, the answer is no. It must be remembered that the energy of the ion is lowered by the additional spherical potential energy term, such as Eq. 4–1. The size of this term depends on the number of ligands about the metal ion in the same way as the Madelung constant depends on the number of nearest neighbors. Therefore, although some lowering of the energy levels may be gained by further removal of a ligand, the total energy is increased because of the change in coulomb energy.

A COMPARISON OF MEDIUM AND STRONG FIELDS

We have seen that the arbitrary separation of crystal-field effects into two divisions depends on:

(1) The spatial extent of the radial wave functions.

(2) The type of ligand.

(3) The energy of interaction of the electron spins of the d-electrons.

The radial wave function effect has been discussed previously, and so we will turn our attention to the ligand type. It is worth noting that the ligands which produce the largest crystal-field splitting are those with a complicated electronic structure which produces a high concentration of electrons. However, if this were the only requirement, the iodide ion should produce a stronger crystal-field effect than chloride ion. This prediction is not observed, and consequently the ligand effect must be more than a strict electrostatic interaction.

The spin-pairing energy is important in deciding whether or not to expect a given ion to show medium- or strong-field effects. For instance, Fe^{3+} shows strong-field splitting with a few ligands such as CN^-, but Co^{3+} is always a strong-field case except for the fluoride ion.

We may make a qualitative estimate of the energy of interaction of the electron spins or, as it is more frequently called, the exchange energy. Hund's rules state that the least energy results from parallel electron spins. Let us assume that if two electrons are parallel, the energy is decreased by an amount c. If there are three parallel electrons, then there are three pairs of parallel spins, and the exchange energy is $3c$. In general, for n parallel electrons the exchange energy is the combination of n electrons taken two at a time, which is $n(n-1)/2$ multiplied by c.

TABLE 4–3

Ion configuration	Medium-field energy	Strong-field energy	Energy difference between strong and medium fields
d^1	$-\frac{2}{5}\Delta$	$-\frac{2}{5}\Delta$	0
d^2	$-\frac{3}{5}\Delta - c$	$-\frac{4}{5}\Delta - c$	$-\Delta/5$
d^3	$-\frac{6}{5}\Delta - 3c$	$-\frac{6}{5}\Delta - 3c$	0
d^4	$-\frac{3}{5}\Delta - 6c$	$-\frac{8}{5}\Delta - 3c$	$-\Delta + 3c$
d^5	$- 10c$	$-2\Delta - 4c$	$-2\Delta + 6c$
d^6	$-\frac{2}{5}\Delta - 10c$	$-\frac{12}{5}\Delta - 6c$	$-2\Delta + 4c$

In the transition from the medium-field to the strong-field case, there may be a decrease in orbital energy but at some sacrifice in exchange energy. The change in orbital energy for an ion is just the energy difference between the case without and that with the crystal-field splitting. For example, in the medium-field case the energy is $-2/5\,\Delta$ for Ti^{3+}. We list in Table 4–3 the stabilization energy for each electron configuration together with the exchange energy for the medium-field case.

The strong-field stabilization energies are just $(-2n\,\Delta)/5$ for $n \leq 6$ and $(-2\Delta/5)(n - m) + (3\Delta/5)m$ for $n > 6$. These energies are also given in Table 4–3. Because octahedral configurations for $n > 6$ in the strong-field case are not observed, the table does not list these cases.

If we assume that c does not change appreciably in going from one configuration to another, then Table 4–3 shows that the d^6-configuration is the most likely to gain energy by pairing electron spins. It gains -2Δ in orbital energy while losing only $+4c$ in exchange energy, which explains the Co^{3+} behavior. The next favorable configurations are the d^4- and d^5-cases, which have the same gain-loss ratio. It is easy to see that as Δ increases, the strong-field case becomes more favorable. For this reason the strong-field case is almost always observed for $4d$- and $5d$-complexes.

OTHER PHYSICAL ASPECTS OF THE CRYSTAL FIELD THEORY

Size. An assumption used in Chapter 1 to obtain a set of ionic radii was that ions are hard spheres. This assumption is not a bad approximation to the actual case if the ion is in an S-state; but if the ion has a d^n electron configuration, the approximation is not so valid. We expect that the radii for all ions with a d^n-configuration should be nearly the same and, in fact, decrease a small amount as the atomic number increases. The reason for this expectation is that the radius of an ion is principally determined by the principal quantum number and effective nuclear charge. As the atomic number increases the radius should decrease a small amount, and the additional d-electrons should thicken the electron cloud.

The effect of the e_g- and t_{2g}-orbitals on the radius is quite different. The t_{2g}-orbitals in an octahedral environment are located away from the ligands with the result that the "radius" is somewhat less than the spatial extent of the wave function. On the other hand, the e_g-orbitals are oriented so that they point toward the ligands, which gives a larger radius because of the electrostatic repulsion.

A plot of the bond distances between the transition metal ions and ligands in a given structural series should show irregularities which are correlated with the occupation of the e_g-orbitals. Let us consider the medium-field octahedral case. The e_g-orbitals are occupied with d^4- and d^5-ions. Spin pairing occurs at d^6, d^7, and d^8 in the t_{2g}-orbitals, and the e_g-orbitals are again filled in for d^9- and d^{10}-ions.

In Fig. 4–23, the observed metal—oxide bond distances are plotted for a number of divalent and trivalent ions. It clearly shows that the bond distance of Mn occurs at a hump in the curve. The internuclear spacings proceed along a smooth curve again until Zn^{2+}, which shows an increased ion size in agreement with the predictions.

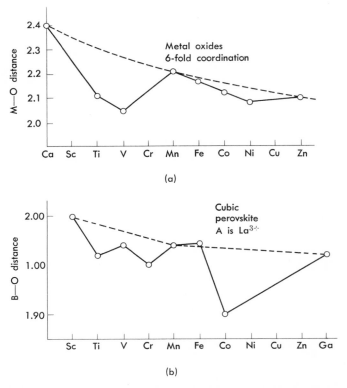

Fig. 4–23. The bond distances of transition metal ions (a) as divalent oxides and (b) as trivalent B ions in the cubic perovskite structure, ABO_3 where the A ion is La^{3+}. [M. H. L. Pryce, *J. Chem. Phys.* **28**, 244 (1958).]

Thermodynamic effects.   The decrease in ionic radius of the $3d$-ions with an increase in the atomic number should cause the lattice energy and heat of hydration to increase.   For the lattice energy, the exact expression is given by Eq. (1–17).   The heat of hydration which corresponds to the heat of the reaction

$$M^{2+}_{(g)} + xH_2O \rightarrow M(H_2O)^{2+}_x$$

will also have a similar dependence on R_0^{-1}, where R_0 is the metal ion—ligand distance.   Since d^0-, d^5-, and d^{10}-ions in a medium crystal field show no field effects, the corresponding heats of hydration should lie on a smooth curve.   The

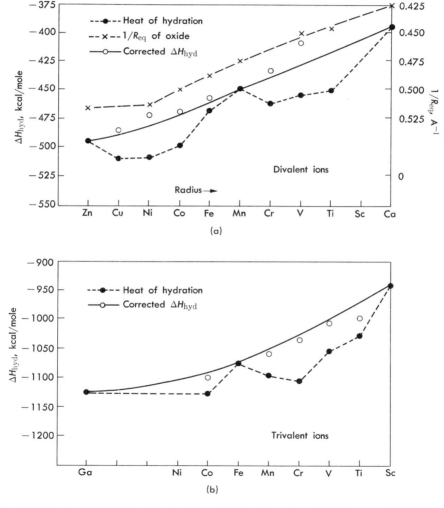

Fig. 4–24. The heat of hydration of the transition metal ions. The reciprocal of the measured bond distance of the metal oxide is also plotted with the divalent ions to show the same general change. Note that the ions are plotted according to increasing size.

other d^n-configuration ions should show an increased heat of hydration because of the additional crystal-field stabilization energy. Figure 4–24 shows this effect for both 2+ and 3+ ions. From spectral analysis we may obtain Δ and, therefore, the stabilization energy which may be subtracted from the heats of hydration. The resulting energy should correspond to the crystal-field free hydration energy, which should show the smooth increase with atomic number as outlined above. The results of such a calculation are also plotted in Fig. 4–24, which shows the correctness of the reasoning.

Pressure effects. The spectra of several transition metal complexes have been measured under hydrostatic pressures as high as 120,000 atmospheres. The effect of high pressure should be to shorten the internuclear distance of the metal ion and ligand. From our point-charge model we saw that Δ varies as a_i^{-5}. Therefore, increasing the pressure should shift the absorption peaks to shorter wave lengths.

As an example of the pressure effect, let us consider the compound $Cr(NH_3)_6Cl_3$. The ground state of Cr^{3+} is $3d^3$, ^4F, which is split into three orbital levels, a singlet and two triplets. The singlet is the ground state, and absorptions are observed arising from transitions from the singlet to the two triplets. The pressure shift of these absorption lines is shown in Fig. 4–25.

At zero pressure, $\Delta = 21{,}500$ cm^{-1}. It is clear from Fig. 4–25 that the two triplets vary differently under hydrostatic pressure. This is not particularly surprising since the mixtures of the e_g- and t_{2g}-orbitals which make up these states are different. The level with the largest admixture of e_g-orbitals should be affected most by pressure effects, because the interaction with the ligands is more pronounced.

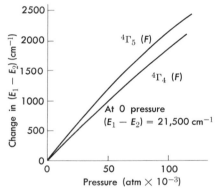

Fig. 4–25. The effect of hydrostatic pressure on the crystal field energy levels of $Cr(NH_3)_6Cl_3$. [R. W. Parsons and H. G. Drickamer, *J. Chem. Phys.* **29**, 930 (1958).]

REFERENCES

BAILER, J. C., Ed., *The Chemistry of Coordination Compounds*, Reinhold, New York, 1956.

BALLHAUSEN, C. J., *Introduction to Ligand Field Theory*, McGraw-Hill, New York, 1962.

BASOLO, F., and R. G. PEARSON, *Mechanism of Inorganic Reactions*, Wiley, New York, 1958.

GRINBERG, A. A., *An Introduction to the Chemistry of Complex Compounds*, Addison-Wesley, Reading, Mass., 1962.

Jorgensen, C. K., *Absorption Spectra and Chemical Bonding in Complexes*, Addison-Wesley, Reading, Mass., 1962.

Orgel, L., *An Introduction to Transition Metal Chemistry: Ligand Field Theory*, Wiley, New York, 1960.

PROBLEMS

1. Show that the isolation of two optical isomers of the compound Co(en)$_3$ is "proof" that it has the octahedral form and not the hexagonal or trigonal prismatic form.

2. Consider the structural isomers for Pt(NH$_3$)$_2$Cl$_2$. How would you determine whether the compound were planar or tetrahedral?

3. Show that a Jahn-Teller distortion of a tetrahedral environment is expected for for d^3, d^4, d^8, and d^9 configurations.

4. Calculate the electron configurations where increases in size of the $3d$ transition metal ions should occur for tetrahedral coordination. Consult a handbook to see whether there is any evidence to support your predictions.

5. Prove that the fourth-order term in an octahedral potential energy expression must be $A(x^4 + y^4 + z^4)$.

6. Using the fact that $x^2 + y^2 + z^2 = r^2$, show that Eq. (4–14) may be written as a sum of a spherically symmetric plus an axially symmetric potential-energy term.

7. Show that $\nabla^2(1/r) = 0$. This equation is known as Laplace's equation. Since Eq. (4–2) must satisfy this equation, show that $C_3 = -2C_2$ in Eq. (4–14), and therefore a tetragonal distortion introduces only one additional constant in the potential energy expression.

8. Show that a rotation of only the triangle of points 1, 2, 3 in Fig. 4–1(b) by $\pi/3$ results in a set of six equivalent points, which is the same as Fig. 4–1(c).

9. Consider the *cis* and *trans* isomers of Co(en)$_2$Cl$_2^+$. Write out all the symmetry operations for each isomer. Draw an energy-level diagram for a d-electron in each compound. What differences are expected?

10. It is sometimes convenient to choose a set of axes of the coordinate system other than those given for the octahedral case in this chapter. Consider the case of choosing a new coordinate system which is obtained from the old system by a rotation by $\pi/4$ about the z-axis. Show that the coordinates are related by

$$z = z', \qquad y = \frac{\sqrt{2}}{2}(x' + y'), \qquad x = \frac{\sqrt{2}}{2}(x' - y'),$$

where x', y', and z' are the coordinates in the rotated system.

11. Using the results of Problem 10, into what functions are the orbitals of Eq. (3–31) changed? Note that orbital designations depend on the axes chosen, but there is no fundamental difference in the symmetry.

12. A single absorption peak is observed for the compound VCl$_4$ at $\tilde{\nu} = 9000 \text{ cm}^{-1}$. What is the value of Δ if the molecule is tetrahedral? What would be your estimate of the value of V^{4+} in an octahedral environment?

13. Using the appropriate Orgel diagram, what value of Δ will fit the spectrum of Cr(H$_2$O)$_6^{3+}$ given in Fig. 4–16?

5
Magnetic Properties of Coordination Compounds

The investigation of the magnetic properties of materials has been a source of structural information for a long time. It has only been during the last fifteen years that this research has come to full fruition with the advent of electron paramagnetic and nuclear paramagnetic resonance techniques. To understand the basis of these methods, it is necessary to recall and understand more thoroughly the characteristics of magnetic phenomena and the interpretation of the macroscopic properties in terms of the microscopic properties, such as angular momentum and crystal fields.

MACROSCOPIC MAGNETIC EFFECTS

If any material is placed in an inhomogeneous magnetic field, there is a force exerted on the material which tends to either pull the material toward the larger field or push the material out of the field. The first case is divided into two subgroups: those materials which have a large force and those with a weak force. The former substances are said to be *ferromagnetic*, and the latter are *paramagnetic*. The compounds which are pushed out of the magnetic field are called *diamagnetic* materials. The forces which diamagnetic materials experience are generally smaller in magnitude than the paramagnetic forces.

Let us analyze the forces on a magnetic material in more detail. From elementary physics we know that the force on a fictitious magnetic monopole is proportional to the magnetic field:

$$\mathbf{f} = m\mathbf{H}. \qquad (5\text{-}1)$$

Let us assume that we have a magnetic dipole $\boldsymbol{\mu}$, which consists of two monopoles of opposite sign separated by a distance $d\mathbf{s}$, as shown in Fig. 5–1. For simplicity we will consider that the dipole is in the xy-plane. A magnetic field $\mathbf{H}$ is applied to the dipole. The resulting force is the sum of

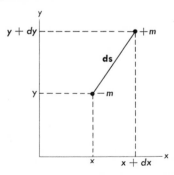

Fig. 5–1. The coordinates of a magnetic dipole in a two-dimensional space.

the forces on the unit poles, which will be zero if the magnetic field does not change over the distance $d\mathbf{s}$. Let us assume that the field does change by an amount, $d\mathbf{H}$. Then

$$\mathbf{f} = -m\mathbf{H} + m(\mathbf{H} + d\mathbf{H}) = m\,d\mathbf{H}. \qquad (5\text{-}2)$$

Since
$$\mathbf{H} = \mathbf{H}(x, y), \tag{5-3}$$

$$d\mathbf{H} = \frac{\partial \mathbf{H}}{\partial x} \, dx + \frac{\partial \mathbf{H}}{\partial y} \, dy. \tag{5-4}$$

Therefore, we have for the force,

$$\mathbf{f} = m \, dx \frac{\partial \mathbf{H}}{\partial x} + m \, dy \frac{\partial \mathbf{H}}{\partial y} \tag{5-5}$$

$$= \mu_x \frac{\partial \mathbf{H}}{\partial x} + \mu_y \frac{\partial \mathbf{H}}{\partial y}, \tag{5-6}$$

where $(d\mathbf{s})^2 = (dx)^2 + (dy)^2$ and μ_i is a component of the magnetic dipole along the ith axis. If we let

$$\boldsymbol{\mu} = \mathbf{i}\mu_x + \mathbf{j}\mu_y \quad \text{and} \quad \nabla = \mathbf{i}\frac{\partial}{\partial x} + \mathbf{j}\frac{\partial}{\partial y},$$

then Eq. (5–6) becomes

$$\mathbf{f} = \boldsymbol{\mu} \cdot \nabla \mathbf{H}, \tag{5-7}$$

which may be directly applied to three dimensions also. Thus we have shown that the force on a magnetic dipole is proportional to the gradient or the slope of the magnetic field.

Suppose we have, instead of a single dipole, a collection of dipoles whose magnetic moment per unit volume is $\mathbf{M}$. And in addition, imagine that the magnetic moment is linearly dependent upon the magnetic field, as would be the case for a random arrangement of dipoles which are aligned more or less depending upon the magnetic field strength:

$$\mathbf{M} = \chi\mathbf{H}. \tag{5-8}$$

We have for the force on a unit volume:

$$\mathbf{f} = \chi\mathbf{H} \cdot \nabla\mathbf{H} = \tfrac{1}{2}\chi\nabla H^2. \tag{5-9}$$

The magnetic moment per unit volume is usually called the *magnetization*, and χ, the proportionality factor, is called the *magnetic susceptibility*.

Equation (5–9) shows that we may classify the magnetic properties of materials according to their susceptibility. If the susceptibility is negative, the material is diamagnetic; if it is positive, the material is paramagnetic or ferromagnetic.

A particularly simple method for measuring the susceptibility is shown in Fig. 5–2. The apparatus consists of a glass tube of cross section A which is suspended from one arm of a balance. The tube is packed with the sample, and the density is measured to correct for the packing error. It is positioned in the magnetic field with one end of the sample in the center of the magnetic field and the other completely out of the field.

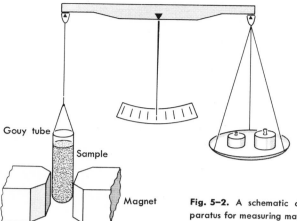

Gouy tube

Sample

Magnet

Fig. 5–2. A schematic drawing of the Gouy apparatus for measuring magnetic susceptibility.

If we let the axis of the tube be the z-axis, then the force in the z-direction due to the magnetization is the integral of a unit volume force over the volume of the tube:

$$F_z = \int f \, dV = \tfrac{1}{2}\chi \int \nabla H^2 \, dV. \tag{5–10}$$

Since $dV = A \, dz$, the force becomes

$$F_z = \tfrac{1}{2}A\chi \int \frac{\partial H^2}{\partial z} \, dz = \tfrac{1}{2}A\chi \int_{z_0}^{z_1} dH^2$$

$$= \tfrac{1}{2}\chi A (H_{z_1}^2 - H_{z_0}^2), \tag{5–11}$$

which may be rewritten as

$$\chi = \frac{2F_z}{A(H_{z_1}^2 - H_{z_0}^2)}. \tag{5–12}$$

The usual technique is to measure the force on a standard due to a given magnetic field and to compare it with the force on the unknown at the same field. The susceptibility of the unknown may be easily found if corrections are made for the change in density of the sample. This method is known as a Gouy measurement.

Another technique is to measure the force on a small sample in a uniform magnetic field gradient. If the field gradient and the sample volume are constant, susceptibilities may be measured by reference to a standard. This measurement is called the Faraday method and is applicable to small samples such as single crystals.

If single crystals are used, it is frequently found that the susceptibility is anisotropic. In fact, for all but cubic materials, the susceptibility is not isotropic. We may see the reason for this by reexamining Eq. (5–8), which is a relationship between two vector quantities. These vectors need not have the same direction, in which case the components of the magnetization are given most generally by

$$M_x = \chi_{xx}H_x + \chi_{xy}H_y + \chi_{xz}H_z,$$
$$M_y = \chi_{yx}H_x + \chi_{yy}H_y + \chi_{yz}H_z, \tag{5–13}$$
$$M_z = \chi_{zx}H_x + \chi_{zy}H_y + \chi_{zz}H_z.$$

Equation (5–13) may also be expressed as a matrix equation:

$$\begin{pmatrix} M_x \\ M_y \\ M_z \end{pmatrix} = \begin{pmatrix} \chi_{xx} & \chi_{xy} & \chi_{xz} \\ \chi_{yx} & \chi_{yy} & \chi_{yz} \\ \chi_{zx} & \chi_{zy} & \chi_{zz} \end{pmatrix} \begin{pmatrix} H_x \\ H_y \\ H_z \end{pmatrix}, \tag{5–13a}$$

where the vectors are written as column matrices and the susceptibility as a 3×3 matrix, called a second-rank tensor. We see that, in general, there are nine components of the susceptibility.

Once again we can investigate the effect of symmetry on a function which this time is the susceptibility tensor. Suppose we have a tetragonal crystal in which the z-axis is not equivalent to the x- or y-axes. If we apply a magnetic field along the x-axis, then from Eq. (5–13) we have

$$M_x = \chi_{xx}H_x, \qquad M_y = \chi_{yx}H_x, \qquad M_z = \chi_{zx}H_x. \tag{5–14}$$

Now let us apply the magnetic field in the negative x-direction. The magnetization in the x-direction must be changed, but the magnetization components along y and z must be invariant because of the 2-fold symmetry of these axes. Therefore, we have

$$-M_x = \chi_{xx}(-H_x), \qquad M_y = \chi_{yx}(-H_x), \qquad M_z = \chi_{zx}(-H_x), \tag{5–15}$$

which, when compared with Eq. (5–14), can only be true if $\chi_{zx} = \chi_{yx} = 0$. In a similar fashion it can be shown that $\chi_{xy} = \chi_{xz} = \chi_{yz} = \chi_{zy} = 0$. We are left with a susceptibility tensor of the form

$$\begin{pmatrix} \chi_{xx} & 0 & 0 \\ 0 & \chi_{yy} & 0 \\ 0 & 0 & \chi_{zz} \end{pmatrix} \tag{5–16}$$

Matrix 5–16 may be simplified further by noting that $\chi_{xx} = \chi_{yy}$ because of the 4-fold symmetry of the z-axis. Therefore, for a tetragonal crystal, two components of the susceptibility tensor must be given.

It is easy to see that for cubic crystals only one susceptibility component is needed, and for crystals with three inequivalent axes, three components are

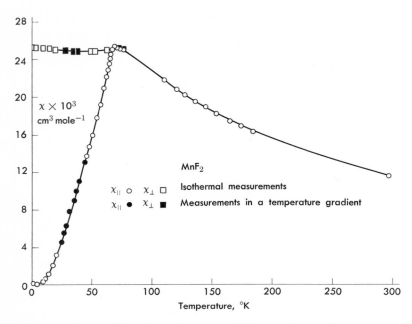

Fig. 5–3. The magnetic susceptibility of a single crystal of MnF₂ as a function of temperature. $X_\perp$ is the susceptibility perpendicular to the c-axis and $X_{||}$ is the parallel susceptibility. [Courtesy of C. Trapp and J. W. Stout.]

TABLE 5–1

THE SUSCEPTIBILITY TENSOR COMPONENTS FOR SOME
SINGLE CRYSTAL MATERIALS*

Compound	Mole susceptibility $\times 10^6$ at room temperature		
	X_1	X_2	X_3
$(NH_4)_2Fe(SO_4)_2 \cdot 6H_2O$	12,410	9,829	12,198
$(NH_4)_2Co(SO_4)_2 \cdot 6H_2O$	11,110	8,088	9,570
$(NH_4)_2Ni(SO_4)_2 \cdot 6H_2O$	4,040	3,929	3,933
$(NH_4)_2Mn(SO_4)_2 \cdot 6H_2O$	13,835	13,826	13,829
$(Rb)_2Mn(SO_4)_2 \cdot 6H_2O$	13,985	13,976	13,978
$(NH_4)_2Zn(SO_4)_2 \cdot 6H_2O$	Diamagnetic		
$NiSO_4 \cdot 7H_2O$	3,012	2,989	3,007
Ferrocene	−99.0	−136.0	−139.9

* To obtain the paramagnetic susceptibility, the following diamagnetic corrections are made (all values are $\times 10^6$): NH_4^+, −13.3; H_2O, −13; SO_4^{2-}, −40.1; metal ion, −12.8.

necessary. For many crystals the axes of symmetry are not at right angles to each other, but it may be shown that a reduction to, at most, three components is always possible.

Many of the values of susceptibility found in the literature are given for powders as determined by the Gouy method. The susceptibility given is a suitable average over all the components.

The results of some single crystal measurements are listed in Table 5–1. The particularly interesting susceptibility of MnF_2 is shown in Fig. 5–3 as a function of absolute temperature. The anisotropy is clearly evident below 70°K.

MICROSCOPIC INTERPRETATION OF MAGNETIC SUSCEPTIBILITY

To use the susceptibility as a structural tool, the chemist must be able to interpret the measurements in terms of the motion of electrons and the intrinsic magnetic moment of the electron. Nuclei also have magnetic properties, but the effects are about 2000 times smaller than the electronic effects.

In Chapter 3, the effect of a magnetic field on an atom was examined by considering the symmetry. It was found that all spin angular momentum and orbital angular momentum degeneracies are removed. The actual calculation of the eigenvalues belonging to the nondegenerate states must be done quantum mechanically, and we will only consider a simple case to illustrate the method. The Hamiltonian is the sum of the free ion Hamiltonian $\mathcal{H}_F$, and the magnetic field Hamiltonian $\mathcal{H}_{\mathrm{mag}}$:

$$\mathcal{H} = \mathcal{H}_F + \mathcal{H}_{\mathrm{mag}}. \tag{5–17}$$

If we solve Schroedinger's equation, the energy belonging to a state ψ is just

$$E = E_F + E_{\mathrm{mag}}, \tag{5–18}$$

providing $\mathcal{H}_{\mathrm{mag}}$ is small compared to $\mathcal{H}_F$.

It may be shown that the magnetic field Hamiltonian is

$$\mathcal{H}_{\mathrm{mag}} = \beta \mathbf{H} \cdot (\mathbf{L} + 2\mathbf{S}), \tag{5–19}$$

where β is called the Bohr magneton, $eh/2mc$. If the magnetic field is along the z-axis, Eq. (5–19) reduces to

$$\mathcal{H}_{\mathrm{mag}} = \beta H_z (L_z + 2S_z). \tag{5–20}$$

The eigenvalues of this Hamiltonian were shown in Chapter 3 to be

$$E = \beta H_z (M_L + 2M_S) \tag{5–21}$$

for a state whose magnetic quantum numbers are M_L and M_S.

We may easily calculate the energy for a magnetic dipole in a magnetic field from Eq. (5–7). The force is the gradient of the potential energy so that

$$f_z = -\frac{\partial E}{\partial z} = -\mu_z \frac{\partial H_z}{\partial z}. \tag{5–22}$$

Upon integration, we obtain

$$E = -\mu_z H_z. \tag{5–23}$$

Comparison of Eqs. (5–21) and (5–23) shows that

$$\mu_z = -\beta(M_L + 2M_S). \tag{5–24}$$

In other words, the paramagnetic dipole moment of a state is dependent simply upon the magnetic quantum numbers.

The magnetic fields which are usually used in the laboratory range as high as 50,000 gauss. A special installation at the National Magnet Laboratory in Cambridge, Mass., produces fields as high as 250,000 gauss. Although we label such fields as strong, it is worth while to calculate the energy splitting of an electronic spin state, $S = \frac{1}{2}$, in this field. The value of β is 9.27×10^{-21} ergs · gauss^{-1}.

$$\begin{aligned}
\Delta E &= E(\tfrac{1}{2}) - E(-\tfrac{1}{2}) \\
&= +2(\tfrac{1}{2} + \tfrac{1}{2})\beta H \\
&= 2(9.27 \times 10^{-21})(250,000) \text{ ergs} \\
&= 4.63 \times 10^{-15} \text{ ergs} \\
&\approx 23 \text{ cm}^{-1}.
\end{aligned}$$

Therefore, the splittings of lines by external magnetic fields are quite small compared to those produced by ligand fields, for example; and we are justified in assuming that $\mathcal{3C}_{\text{mag}}$ is small compared with $\mathcal{3C}_F$.

If we know the eigenfunctions of an atom, it is possible to calculate the magnetic moments and suitably average the result to obtain the susceptibility. As an example, consider an ion such as Mn^{2+}, which has zero orbital angular momentum in its ground state. The spin angular-momentum quantum number is $\frac{5}{2}$ arising from the $3d^5$-configuration. In the absence of any external influences, the magnetic moment of a collection of manganous ions would align up with the magnetic field. However, thermal agitation prevents the alignment and cancels some of the magnetization. Consequently, the resultant magnetization is temperature dependent. The higher the temperature, the smaller the magnetization in a given field.

The system may be described also in terms of its energy-level diagram. If there is no thermal energy, all atoms will be in their ground state. The resulting magnetization will be a maximum. As the temperature increases, the number of atoms in states other than the ground state will increase simply because of the thermal energy. The number of ions with a given energy is dependent upon the total number of ions, the energy, and the temperature. Such a system is describable by the Boltzmann distribution law which states that the number of ions, n_i, in an energy state E_i above the ground state at a temperature T is

$$n_i = \frac{n_0 e^{-E_i/kT}}{\sum_i e^{-E_i/kT}}. \tag{5-25}$$

If the $\sum_i n_i$ is the number of ions in a unit volume, then the magnetization is

$$M = \sum_i n_i \mu_i. \tag{5-26}$$

If we substitute Eq. (5–23) or, more exactly, use $\mu_i = -\partial E_i/\partial H$, then we obtain for an ion with zero orbital angular momentum,

$$M = \sum_i n_i(-\partial E_i/\partial H) = \sum_i -2m_i\beta n_i$$

$$= \frac{n_0 \sum_i -2m_i\beta e^{-2m_i\beta H/kT}}{\sum_i e^{-2m_i\beta H/kT}}. \tag{5-27}$$

Using Eq. (5–8), we find that the susceptibility is

$$\chi = \frac{n_0}{H} \frac{\sum_i -2m_i\beta e^{-2m_i\beta H/kT}}{\sum_i e^{-2m_i\beta H/kT}}. \tag{5-28}$$

The thermal energy kT at room temperature is about 210 cm^{-1}, and the magnetic energy is about 1 cm^{-1} for a field of 8000 gauss. Therefore, we can expand the exponential and carry out the sum, keeping only the first two terms. The values of m_i run from s to $-s$ so that the sum is

$$\chi = \frac{-2n_0\beta \sum_{-s}^{s} m_i[1 - (2m_i\beta H)/kT]}{H \sum_{-s}^{s} [1 - (2m_i\beta H)/kT]}. \tag{5-29}$$

Now

$$\sum_{-s}^{s} 1 = 2s + 1, \qquad \sum_{-s}^{s} m_i = 0, \qquad \sum_{-s}^{s} m_i^2 = \tfrac{1}{3}(2s + 1)(s)(s + 1).$$

Therefore,

$$\chi = \frac{4n_0\beta^2 S(S + 1)}{3kT}, \tag{5-30}$$

which has the form

$$\chi = \frac{nC}{T}. \tag{5-31}$$

Equation (5–31) is known as Curie's Law.

In Fig. 5–4 the reciprocal of the susceptibility is drawn as a function of temperature for a typical paramagnetic salt exhibiting spin-only susceptibility. The slope of the curve is $3k/4n_0\beta^2(S)(S + 1)$.

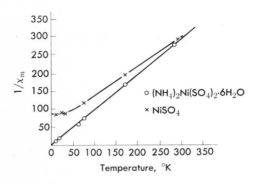

Fig. 5–4. The magnetic susceptibility of powdered $(NH_4)_2Ni(SO_4)_2 \cdot 6H_2O$ and $NiSO_4$ as a function of temperature.

If the above calculation had been performed using as the energy $-\mu_i H$, then the classical expression for the susceptibility would be found as

$$\chi = \frac{n_0 \mu^2}{3kT}. \tag{5–32}$$

A comparison of Eq. (5–32) with Eq. (5–30) gives the root-mean-square magnetic moment μ_m:

$$\mu_m = 2\beta \sqrt{S(S+1)}. \tag{5–33}$$

For an atom with n unpaired electrons, $S = n(\frac{1}{2})$. By substituting into Eq. (5–33), μ_m is calculated in terms of n:

$$\mu_m = 2\beta \sqrt{n(\tfrac{1}{2})(n/2+1)} = \beta \sqrt{n(n+2)}. \tag{5–34}$$

Similar calculations can be made for an ion with orbital angular momentum as well as with spin angular momentum. The susceptibility expression becomes

$$\chi = \frac{n_0 \beta^2 [4S(S+1) + L(L+1)]}{3kT}. \tag{5–35}$$

The effect of orbital angular momentum is to increase the susceptibility from a spin-only susceptibility.

In addition to these derived equations there is always a diamagnetic contribution to the susceptibility. The student should be familiar with Lenz' law, which states that the current induced in a coil by a moving magnetic field produces a magnetic field tending to oppose the moving field. In a similar manner a magnetic field on an atom tends to induce a current, which means a change in the size of the orbit of an electron. The induced magnetic field tends to push the sample out of the field. The susceptibility contribution is opposite in sign to that previously calculated for the paramagnetic terms and is given by

$$\chi_d = -\frac{n_0 e^2}{3mc^2} \sum_i \overline{r_i^2}, \tag{5–36}$$

where c is the velocity of light. The term $\overline{r_i^2}$ is the average of the square of the radius of the orbit of the electron. The total susceptibility equation may be written in the general Langevin-Debye form,

$$\chi = n_0 \left(\frac{C}{T} - \alpha \right). \qquad (5\text{-}37)$$

For many paramagnetic materials the behavior of the susceptibility is altered as the temperature is lowered. The alteration is of two forms, as shown in Fig. 5–5. The first example is that of a transition from a paramagnetic to a ferromagnetic state. The susceptibility increases rapidly as the temperature is lowered and may be represented by an equation of the form

$$\chi = \frac{C}{T - \Delta}, \qquad (5\text{-}38)$$

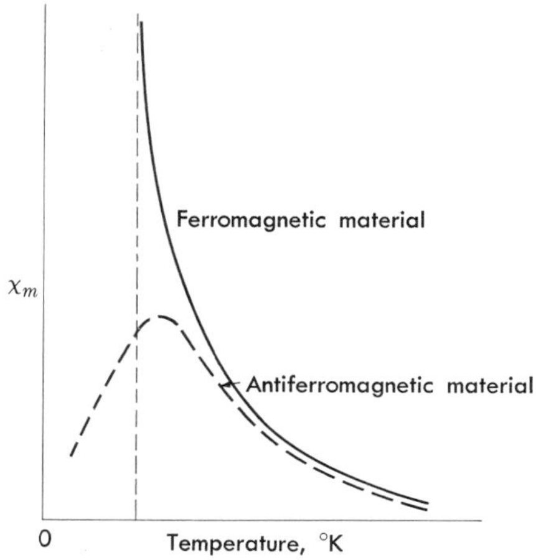

Fig. 5–5. A graph of the susceptibility of a ferromagnetic and antiferromagnetic material as a function of temperature.

where Δ is a characteristic temperature of the material. The second case shown in the figure is called antiferromagnetism, because the results are, in a sense, opposite to that of ferromagnetism. In this case, at a critical temperature the magnetization begins to decrease to zero.

The cause of both behaviors of the susceptibility is the result of cooperative interactions of the spin and orbital angular momenta of the ions in the crystal. In one case, the ferromagnetic state, the moments of each ion are all aligned in the same direction at zero temperature. In the antiferromagnetic case, there is not random alignment but an ordering such that in simple cases every other ion has its moment aligned opposite to its neighbors.

ELECTRON PARAMAGNETIC RESONANCE

The measurement of magnetic susceptibility by a static magnetic field is a gross measurement, because the interpretation involves a sum over all energy states. For a few years prior to World War II, attempts were made to measure directly the separation of magnetic states by absorption of radio frequency radiation. Work was suspended during the war and it wasn't until 1945 that Zavoisky in Russia was able to perform a successful measurement. Since that time, the technique, which is known as electron paramagnetic resonance, has been applied to a wide variety of systems. The resulting detailed information has been tremendously useful both theoretically and practically.

To understand the basic ideas involved, consider an ion with a ground state having no orbital angular momentum but a spin angular momentum of $S = 1$. In a magnetic field this state is split into three levels according to Eq. (5–21).

Figure 5–6 shows that the energy difference between adjacent states is $2\beta H$. If the system is irradiated with a frequency ν such that $h\nu = \Delta E$, energy will be absorbed from the radiation field. The condition for absorption is:

$$h\nu = 2\beta H \qquad (5\text{–}39)$$

or

$$\frac{\nu}{H} = \frac{2\beta}{h}. \qquad (5\text{–}40)$$

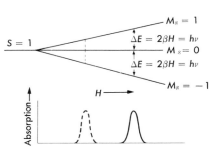

Fig. 5–6. The Zeeman energy-level diagram for an $S = 1$ state. The electron paramagnetic resonance absorption is given for a fixed frequency.

The right-hand side of Eq. (5–40) is a constant, so that the ratio of ν/H is fixed for isolated spin systems.

Let us consider this system in more detail. Figure 5–6 illustrates two absorption lines which will lie on top of each other. These lines are allowed by the selection rule that $\Delta M_S = \pm 1$. The transition from the $M_S = -1$ to the $M_S = 1$ level is not allowed quantum mechanically and consequently is not observed. Initially the electrons will have a Boltzmann distribution among the energy states. The observed absorption of radiation is the result of two simultaneous processes: the movement of electrons from a lower to a higher state and the movement of electrons from a higher to a lower state. The probabilities of each of these transitions are equal but because of the Boltzmann difference in population, there are more transitions to a higher state with the net result of absorption. If the radiation is sufficiently intense to overcome any process by which electrons can go from a higher to a lower state without radiating, then the population of all levels will become equal, and no net absorption will occur. The system then has an infinite temperature, as can be seen from Eq. (5–25).

Simple systems such as those described above are not usually found in nature. There are many local fields possible which serve to complicate the energy levels but at the same time give more information. We will illustrate three such fields.

The first complication is that for spin systems with $S > \frac{1}{2}$. Usually there is found a splitting of the ground state at zero magnetic field. The splitting results from interaction of the spin state and some higher state. In addition, the factor of 2 in Eq. (5–39) is modified and will be somewhat greater or less than 2, depending on the exact interaction. However, the general expression for resonance absorption will still be

$$h\nu = g\beta H. \qquad (5\text{–}41)$$

Suppose that the example of absorption among levels arising from a spin triplet is modified, as shown in Fig. 5–7. The two allowed absorptions are now resolved. Depending upon the size of the zero-field splitting and the frequency, the actual magnetic field at which absorption occurs will vary. From the measured frequency and magnetic field it is possible to calculate the value of the

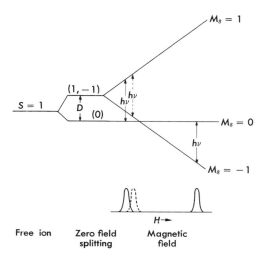

Fig. 5-7. The Zeeman energy-level diagram of a spin triplet split by a zero-field splitting.

zero-field splitting. Splittings as large as several wave numbers and as small as 10^{-4} cm^{-1} have been observed.

A second local magnetic field effect results from the interaction of the electron magnetic moment with the nuclear magnetic moment μ_n. Such a nucleus has a nonzero spin angular momentum which is given the symbol I. Since this is a dipole-dipole interaction, the potential energy will be of the form $A'\mu_n \cdot \mu_e$. Quantum mechanically, we may write the perturbing Hamiltonian as $A\mathbf{I} \cdot \mathbf{S}$, since the dipole moment is simply proportional to the spin angular-momentum operator. To see how this term affects the electron spin-energy levels of Fig. 5–1, let us calculate the new energies for $I = 1$. We may to a good approximation use just the z-components of I and S if $g\beta H \gg A$, in which case we have for the Hamiltonian,

$$\mathcal{H} = g\beta H S_z + A I_z S_z. \qquad (5\text{--}42)$$

For $S = 1$, the energy levels are:

$$
\begin{array}{llll}
M_I = 1 & M_S = 1 & E_1 = g\beta H + A \\
0 & 1 & E_2 = g\beta H \\
-1 & 1 & E_3 = g\beta H - A \\
1 & 0 & E_4 = 0 \\
0 & 0 & E_5 = 0 & (5\text{--}43) \\
-1 & 0 & E_6 = 0 \\
1 & -1 & E_7 = -g\beta H - A \\
0 & -1 & E_8 = -g\beta H \\
-1 & -1 & E_9 = -g\beta H + A
\end{array}
$$

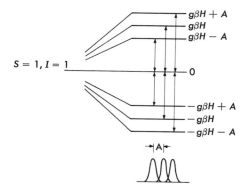

Fig. 5–8. The energy-level diagram for a spin triplet with a nuclear spin of 1 in a strong magnetic field. The electron paramagnetic resonance absorption is also given.

Therefore, each of the levels in Fig. 5–6 is split into triplets giving a total of nine levels. The selection rule for absorption $\Delta M_S = \pm 1$ remains, but now there is an additional requirement of $\Delta M_I = 0$. Figure 5–8 shows that three lines result with a spacing equal to the value of A measured in gauss. In general, the number of observed lines due to the nuclear spin is $2I + 1$. The size of A is indicative of the interaction of the electrons with the nucleus. If it is large, the interaction is large, and vice versa.

The last effect is that of orbital angular momentum on the energy levels. As we saw in Chapter 4, the orbital motion of electron is strongly affected by crystal fields. The resulting ground state may or may not have orbital degeneracy remaining. If orbital effects remain, the result is to produce a resonance absorption which is dependent upon the angle of the magnetic field with respect to the crystal axes. In addition, the values of g are generally very different from two. For this reason much of the research with this technique has been done with single crystals, because powders and solutions give only an averaged result.

Magnetic fields obtainable in a laboratory are in the range of 0–15,000 gauss. From Eq. (5–40) we find that the frequency necessary to induce transitions at a field of 10,000 gauss is approximately 30,000 megacycles per second, which corresponds to an energy of one wave number. Therefore, the production and detection of wave lengths near one centimeter requires the use of microwave techniques. Unfortunately, the presently available equipment is essentially monochromatic and a continuous range in frequency may be approximated only by several different sets of relatively expensive apparatus. In general, the method of observing absorption is to keep the frequency fixed and vary the magnetic field. Obviously, a serious disadvantage is that the energy levels may never match the frequency used at any magnetic field available.

APPLICATION OF SUSCEPTIBILITY AND ELECTRON PARAMAGNETIC RESONANCE MEASUREMENTS TO COORDINATION COMPOUNDS

Medium fields. Table 5–2 shows the experimental results for the magnetic moment in units of Bohr magnetons derived from susceptibility measurements for the 3d-transition group of the periodic table. The values given are repre-

TABLE 5-2

Ion	Configuration	$[\overline{\mu^2}]^{1/2}_{exp}$	$2\sqrt{S(S+1)}$	$\sqrt{4S(S+1)+L(L+1)}$
Ti^{3+}, V^{4+}, Mn^{6+}	d^1	1.71–1.73	1.73	3.01
V^{3+}	d^2	2.75–2.85	2.83	4.49
Cr^{3+}, V^{2+}	d^3	3.82–3.90	3.87	5.21
Cr^{2+}, Mn^{3+}	d^4	4.88	4.91	5.50
Fe^{3+}, Mn^{2+}	d^5	5.61–5.88	5.92	5.92
Fe^{2+}, Co^{3+}	d^6	5.2–5.5	4.91	5.50
Co^{2+}	d^7	4.4–5.2	3.87	5.21
Ni^{2+}	d^8	2.80–3.50	2.83	4.49
Cu^{2+}	d^9	1.81–2.02	1.73	3.01

sentative of the values found experimentally for alums, oxides, halides, and other ligands which would be classified as causing medium electric fields. It is clear that the susceptibility is adequately described by the assumption that the ground state has no orbital angular momentum with poorer agreement for ions with more than five d-electrons.

Let us review what we predict on the basis of the previous chapter. In a cubic octahedral environment, we expect to find orbital singlets lowest for ions with d^3-, d^5-, and d^8-configurations. All other configurations give orbitally degenerate ground states in a cubic field which would contribute substantially to the susceptibility. Therefore, we must not have pure cubic environments for any of the compounds of ions with d^1-, d^2-, d^4-, d^6-, or d^9-configurations. Again, from our previous knowledge we know that any ion with orbital angular momentum will tend to cause a rearrangement of the surroundings by the Jahn-Teller effect. In essence, each ion ends up with no orbital degeneracy which contributes to the susceptibility.

In our analysis of the susceptibility, we have simply assumed that the energy levels are of the form

$$E_i = g\beta M_i H. \tag{5-44}$$

However, from the discussion in Chapter 4 and the introduction to the techniques of electron paramagnetic resonance, it is clear that the magnetic energy levels may be much more complicated than those given by Eq. (5-44). In fact, exact expressions for the energies may be obtained from resonance experiments. The following three examples illustrate the calculations and results for a medium crystal field:

(1) Cr^{3+}, a spin quartet in a cubic field with hyperfine structure.

(2) Ni^{2+}, a spin triplet in an axial field.

(3) Cu^{2+}, an orbitally degenerate ion in a cubic field.

EXAMPLE 1. We found in Chapter 4 that Cr^{3+} with its d^3-configuration has an orbital singlet ground state in a cubic field. The next state, a triplet, is about 20,000 cm^{-1} higher in energy. At room temperature, kT is about 210 cm^{-1} so that in any calculation involving a Boltzmann distribution the triplet may be neglected. Therefore, the system may be simply regarded as a spin quartet, because the parallel electron spins require that $S = \frac{3}{2}$.

A magnetic field will split the quartet, and transitions are observed in a paramagnetic resonance experiment between adjacent levels, as shown in Fig. 5–9(a). The experimental curve of Cr^{3+} in a single crystal of MgO displayed as the derivative is shown in Fig. 5–9(b). A single intense line is observed with a g-value of 1.9800. The g-value of the line does not change as a function of the orientation of the crystal in the magnetic field, which indicates that the chromium ions are in a lattice site with high symmetry. The reduction in the value of g from 2 results from a small interaction of the orbital singlet with the next highest triplet. The calculated effective magnetic moment is 1.9800 $\times$ $[S(S + 1)]^{1/2} = 3.83$ Bohr magnetons.

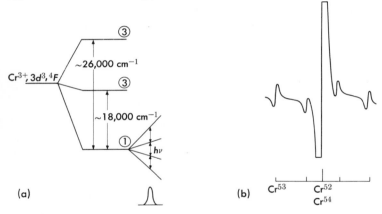

Fig. 5–9. (a) The energy-level diagram of Cr^{3+} in a cubic field. (b) The observed electron paramagnetic resonance absorption of Cr^{3+} as a function of magnetic field. The curves are derivatives of the absorption curves.

Figure 5–9(b) also shows two small peaks on either side of the major peak. They are evenly spaced with an overall spacing of 48 gauss. These lines arise from the Cr^{53} isotope which is 9.6% of the natural abundance. It has a nuclear spin of $\frac{3}{2}$, since the number of lines is $2I + 1$. Using Eq. (5–42) the nuclear-spin electron-spin parameter, A, is calculated to be 16.0 $\times 10^{-4}$ cm^{-1}.

EXAMPLE 2. The ground state of Ni^{2+} has a Hund ground state of $3d^8$, ^3F. In a cubic field the 7-fold orbital level is split into two triplets and a singlet with the latter lowest in the same manner as Cr^{3+}. If the cubic field is distorted by moving the ligands on the z-axis toward the nickel ion, further splitting occurs among the orbital triplets. In fact, because of an interaction of the triplets some of the spin degeneracy of the singlet is removed. The situation is illustrated in Fig. 5–10.

In Chapter 4 we have already considered the effect of an axial electric field on a P-state. The results are applicable to any 3-fold degenerate state; that is, a triplet is split into a doublet and a singlet in an axial field. Let us call the energy difference D. Since by symmetry we saw that the p_x- and p_y-orbitals are degenerate, the same situation exists for the $M_S = 1$ and $M_S = -1$ levels. The application of a magnetic field to the sys-

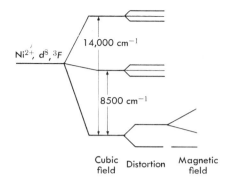

Fig. 5–10. The energy-level diagram of Ni^{2+} in a cubic field and tetragonal field.

tem removes all degeneracy, and the energy levels for H parallel to the z-axis are given by

$$M_S = 1 \quad E_1 = g_z\beta H + D,$$
$$0 \quad E_0 = 0, \tag{5-45}$$
$$-1 \quad E_{-1} = -g_z\beta H + D,$$

where the sign and magnitude of D are determined by experiment. Figure 5–7 is a diagram of the energy levels of Eq. (5–45).

Let us consider the results for the Tutton salt, $(NH_4)_2Ni(SO_4)_2 \cdot 6H_2O$, at room temperature as a specific example. X-ray data for the isomorphous magnesium salt show that each metal ion is surrounded by a distorted octahedron of water molecules. The metal oxygen distances are

$$2.083 \pm 0.005 \text{ A}, \quad 2.073 \pm 0.005 \text{ A}, \quad \text{and} \quad 2.051 \pm 0.005 \text{ A}.$$

We may consider that the nickel salt is quite similar and has two water molecules closer to the nickel ion than the other four which are in a plane. Let us call the shorter distance the z-axis.

Electron paramagnetic resonance has been observed for the $\Delta M_S = \pm 1$ transitions. From measurements of the frequency and magnetic field the value of g_z is found to be 2.25 and D is -2.24 cm^{-1}. The deviation of g from 2 is an indication of the admixture of higher states with the ground state which may be calculated from a knowledge of the energy level diagram.

Let us recalculate the magnetic susceptibility using Eq. (5–45) instead of omitting the zero-field splitting D. We find that

$$\chi_z = \frac{n_0/H[-g_z\beta e^{-(g_z\beta H + D)/kT} + 0e^{-0/kT} + g_z e^{-(-g_z\beta H + D)/kT}]}{e^{-(g_z\beta H + D)/kT} + 1 + e^{-(-g_z\beta H + D)/kT}}. \tag{5-46}$$

At room temperature, kT is about 210 cm^{-1}. Therefore, we can expand the exponentials and retain only the first two terms:

$$\chi_z = \frac{n_0[2g_z^2\beta^2 e^{-D/kT}]}{kT(1 + 2e^{-D/kT})}, \tag{5-47}$$

which for $D/kT \ll 1$ reduces to

$$\chi_z = \frac{2n_0 g_z^2 \beta^2 (1 - D/kT)}{kT(1 + 2 - 2D/kT)} = \frac{2n_0 g_z^2 \beta^2}{3kT}\left(1 - \frac{D}{kT}\right). \tag{5-48}$$

Substitution of the measured values of g_z and D gives for the mole susceptibility, 4260×10^{-6}. The measured value of χ_1 from Table 5–1 which we may
associate with χ_z, is 4230×10^{-6} when corrected for the diamagnetic susceptibility. If Eq. (5–30) had been used, the calculated value would be 3359×10^{-6}.

It should be clear from this example that the effect of the crystal field may
have a large influence on the susceptibility. The effect of D is to either increase
or decrease the susceptibility depending upon the sign. We might expect from
the crystallographic distances that the crystal field is rhombic rather than
tetragonal. This is actually found to be true, and a detailed analysis must
include a small splitting of the $M_S = 1$ and $M_S = -1$ levels.

EXAMPLE 3. Cu^{2+} has a $3d^9$ free ion configuration. The resulting ^2D-state is
split in an octahedral field to give an orbital doublet as the lowest energy level.
We found in Chapter 4 that such states have an inherent Jahn-Teller instability
and the surroundings of the ion move to form a noncubic field. The orbital
doublet is split into two singlets which are still doubly spin degenerate. A magnetic field will remove any further degeneracy, and paramagnetic resonance is
observed for the lower spin doublet. Figure 5–11 shows the energy-level diagram. The measured g-value is dependent on the extent of the distortion and is
generally larger than 2. Similar effects are observed for d^1-, d^2-, d^4-, d^6-, and
d^7-ions.

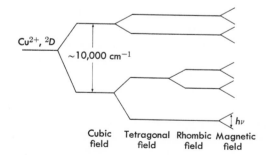

$Cu^{2+}, {}^2D$

$\sim 10,000 \text{ cm}^{-1}$

$h\nu$

Cubic   Tetragonal Rhombic Magnetic
field   field   field   field

Fig. 5–11. The energy-level diagram of Cu^{2+} in various crystal fields.

Strong fields. Table 5–3 is a list of experimental magnetic moments for oc-
tahedrally coordinated $4d$- and $5d$-ions together with some cyanide complexes
of $3d$-ions. The magnetic moments for d^1, d^2, and d^3 approximate the spin-
only moments of Table 5–2. This behavior is to be expected for strong field

ions because there is little difference between the medium- and strong-field cases for these configurations. The magnetic moments for d^4, d^5, and d^6 depart markedly from the spin-only formula. The diamagnetism of the d^6-compounds is easily understood to be the result of filling the t_{2g}-orbital. The calculations for the d^4- and d^5-case are somewhat more difficult but may be broadly interpreted as resulting from the spin pairing of the electrons. We have remarked earlier that states with orbital angular momentum must contribute to the magnetic moment. Therefore, any accurate calculations of the susceptibility for a pure cubic field must include this contribution, which, however, is beyond the scope of this book.

TABLE 5–3

The Experimental Magnetic Moments of some 4d- and 5d-ions

Ion	Configuration	$[\overline{\mu^2}]^{1/2}_{\text{exp}}$	Ion	Configuration	$[\overline{\mu^2}]^{1/2}_{\text{exp}}$
Mo^{5+}	d^1	1.51–1.80	Os^{4+}	d^4	1.3–1.7
W^{4+}	d^2	2.2	Ru^{3+}	d^5	1.88–2.07
Re^{5+}		1.53–2.05	Os^{3+}		1.6–1.9
M^{3+}	d^3	3.70–3.87	Ir^{4+}		
Tc^{4+}		3.73–4.14	$IrCl_6^{3-}$	d^6	
Re^{4+}		2.9–3.3	$Fe(CN)_6^{4-}$		Diamagnetic
Ru^{5+}		3.4–3.7	$Co(CN)_6^{3-}$		
Os^{5+}		3.0–3.3	Pd^{3+}	d^7	2.05
Re^{3+}	d^4	0.47–2.13	Ag^{2+}	d^9	1.6–2.0

Pure cubic fields are difficult to find, especially for strong crystal fields. Distortions readily occur, and orbital singlets generally result. The following examples illustrate this effect upon the magnetic properties.

Consider a d^4-ion such as Re^{3+} or Os^{4+} in a tetragonal field, such that distortion is along the z-axis. The energy-level diagram is shown in Fig. 5–12, where the splittings due to the tetragonal field are small compared to those of the cubic field. A modification of Hund's rules applies to the lower states, namely, that there is maximum spin multiplicity for the electrons with these energies. Consequently, for a d^4-configuration two electrons are paired in the state labeled $|a\rangle$, and two unpaired electrons are in the state $|b\rangle$. The electrons in $|b\rangle$ are the only ones which contribute to the paramagnetism. There can be no resultant orbital angular momentum because of the Pauli principle. Therefore, the effective magnetic moment must come from the electron spin, which agrees with the observations in Table 5–3. It must be emphasized that this conclusion may be modified depending upon the nature of the distortion and the splitting in the energy-level diagram.

The second example is that of $Ni(CN)_4^{2-}$ which we considered in detail in Chapter 4. We saw that the optical spectrum was quite different from that of octahedral nickel complexes. The difference was explained by the fact that the

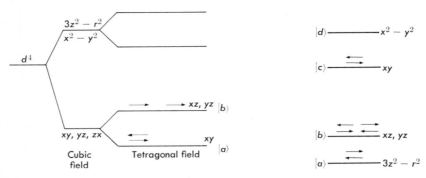

Fig. 5–12. The energy-level diagram of a d^4 configuration in a strong cubic field with a small tetragonal distortion.

Fig. 5–13. The energy-level diagram of Ni^{2+}, $3d^8$, in a square planar complex.

structure was square planar. The energy diagram for a square planar complex is reproduced in Fig. 5–13. The eight d-electrons are distributed with two in state $|a\rangle$, four in state $|b\rangle$, and two in state $|c\rangle$. The result is that all electrons must be paired and the complex is diamagnetic.

These examples serve to show that structural information must be used to understand the results of paramagnetic resonance and magnetic susceptibility measurements. Conversely, the study of electron resonance and magnetic susceptibility data is of tremendous help in obtaining the detailed structure of paramagnetic compounds.

WAVE FUNCTION INFORMATION FROM ELECTRON PARAMAGNETIC RESONANCE

We have placed most of the emphasis in these last two chapters on the nature of the energy-level diagrams of ions in various environments. However, it would be of more value to obtain accurate wave functions, because any measurable quantity could be calculated with the proper Hamiltonian. We have seen how symmetry arguments can be used to give the proper angular wave functions, so that accurate radial wave functions are necessary for fuller understanding. With the use of high-speed computers, theoretical advances in this direction have been made in recent years. Experimentally, paramagnetic resonance has afforded another method to get this information.

If the electron paramagnetic resonance of a dilute crystal of K_2IrCl_6 in K_2PtCl_6 is examined, the spectrum in Fig. 5–14 is found. Ir^{4+} has a $5d^5$-configuration and, in a strong cubic field, has one unpaired electron in the t_{2g}-orbitals. A magnetic field removes the remaining 2-fold degeneracy, and paramagnetic resonance should show a single line corresponding to transitions in this doublet. Figure 5–14 shows this absorption, but it is clearly made up of several lines. Iridium does have two isotopes each with a nuclear spin of $\frac{3}{2}$, but this is insufficient to account for the observed spectrum. We know, however,

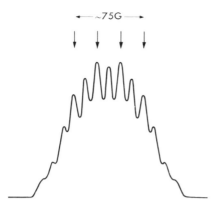

Fig. 5–14. The electron paramagnetic resonance of K_2IrCl_6 in K_2PtCl_6. The four arrows show the splitting due to a single chloride ion and a given isotope of Ir. [J. Owen, *Disc. Faraday Soc.* **19**, 132 (1955).]

that there are six chlorides surrounding each Ir^{4+}. Each chloride also has a nuclear spin of $\frac{3}{2}$. By taking into account the interaction of the unpaired electron with the chlorine nuclei as well as the iridium nucleus, satisfactory fitting of the spectrum can be accomplished. The electrons may no longer be considered to be localized on the metal ion but are spread out on the ligands. To the chemist, this description is simply that of a covalent ionic bond between the ligand and the metal ion. The wave function for complete description must now be a molecular wave function. There are but a few methods for constructing molecular wave functions and the most fruitful is the linear combination of atomic orbitals or LCAO method. In any method, the resulting molecular wave function must have the symmetry of the molecule. For instance if the central metal ion has a $d_{x^2-y^2}$ orbital, the ligand orbital which combines with the metal orbital must have the same transformation properties as $x^2 - y^2$ in the symmetry group of the molecule. Since our previous discussions in this chapter and Chapter 4 about energy splittings were based solely on symmetry arguments, the results obtained are true whether or not the ligands are considered in the wave function.

The advantage of using the molecular orbital theory for coordination compounds or, as it is called, the ligand field theory is that calculations can be made of the covalency of the bonds involved. In addition, charge transfer spectra are readily understood in terms of a complete molecular orbital energy-level diagram.

REFERENCES

CARRINGTON, A., and H. C. LONGUET-HIGGINS, "Electron Paramagnetic Resonance of Transition Metal Complexes," *Quart. Rev.* (London) **14**, 427 (1960).

COTTON, F. A., and G. WILKENSON, *Advanced Inorganic Chemistry*, Interscience, New York, 1962.

KITTEL, C., *Introduction to Solid-State Physics*, Wiley, New York, 1956.

LEWIS, J., and R. G. WILKINS, Eds., *Modern Coordination Chemistry*, Interscience, New York, 1960.

PAKE, G. E., *Paramagnetic Resonance*, Benjamin, New York, 1962.

PROBLEMS

1. From the data of Table 5–1, calculate the paramagnetic susceptibility of the powder of each compound. Calculate the number of Bohr magnetons and compare with the values given in Table 5–2.

2. Suppose a student decides to use the earth's magnetic field rather than a laboratory magnet field to do paramagnetic resonance experiments. From a handbook find a representative value of the earth's field and calculate the frequency at which resonance would occur for $g = 2$.

3. Consider a V^{2+} ion in a cubic field. The most abundant isotope is V^{51}, which has a nuclear spin of $\frac{7}{2}$. Calculate the ground-state energies in the presence of a magnetic field. Draw an energy-level diagram of your results.

4. If, in Problem 3, an axial field is present, what will be the number of lines observed in a paramagnetic resonance experiment without the hyperfine interaction? What will be the number of lines observed with hyperfine interaction? Draw a sketch of the absorption versus magnetic field at constant frequency for both cases.

5. Silver (III) has been prepared in a limited number of compounds, including an iodate. Draw an energy-level diagram of the orbital levels. Would you expect the compounds to be paramagnetic or diamagnetic?

6. In a single crystal of ZnF_2, a rutile structure, in which Mn^{2+} has substitutionally replaced some of the Zn^{2+} sites, a superhyperfine interaction with the nuclei of the F^- ions is observed. However, for Cr^{3+} in a similar site in ZnF_2, no superhyperfine interaction is observed. Account for these findings.

7. Magnetic susceptibilities are frequently expressed in the form of Eq. (5–38), which is known as the Curie-Weiss Law. Assume that Δ is less than T and expand the denominator in a power series. Compare the result with Eq. (5–48).

Index

Layer lattice, 28
Ligands, 73
Line widths, 91
Linear combinations of functions, 31, 57

Madelung constant, 21
Magnetic dipole moment, 106
Magnetic susceptibility, 101
   microscopic interpretation, 105
   table, 104
   tensor, 103
Magnetization, 101
Maxwell, 40
Medium electric fields, 83, 94, 113
Melting points of alkali halides, 26
Metallic crystals, 14
Miller indices, 2
Molecular crystals, 29
Molecular orbitals, 118
Moseley, 35

NaCl structure, 18
Neutron diffraction, 33

Operators, 50, 57
Optical spectra, of coordination
      compounds, 86
   to obtain Δ, 87
Orgel diagrams, 89

Packing fraction, 17
Paramagnetism, 100
Phase angle, 42
Potential energy, 16
   of octahedral electric field, 77
Primitive unit cell, 11
p-state in axial electric field, 61

Quantum mechanics, 49

Radian wave equation, 52
Reduced mass, 50
Reflection, 5
Resolving power, 32

Rotating crystal x-ray diffraction, 38
Rubidium halides, 18
Rutile lattice, 18

Scattering, 36
Schrödinger equation, 51
Screening constant, 20
Space lattice, 13
Spectrum of hydrogen, 56
Spectrum ranges, 47
Sphalerite, 27
Spherical coordinates, 51
Square planar complexes, 93
Stabilization energies, 95
Stacking fault, 15
Steno, Nicolaus, 1
Stereographic projection, 2
Stereoisomerism, 71
Strong electric field, 83, 90, 94, 116
Structure factor, 44
Symmetry, of cube, 5
   of electric fields, 58
   of function, 6
   of magnetic field, 79
   of nonoctahedral electric field, 80
   of octahedral electric field, 79
   of structure factors, 45
   of tetragonal prism, 5

Terms, 66
Thermal neutrons, 33
Three-dimensional space groups, 14

Unit cells, three-dimensional, 8, 11
   two-dimensional, 6, 10

Wavelength, 32
Werner, Alfred, 71
Wigner-Seitz cell, 13

X-ray, 10
X-ray spectrum, 34

Zeeman effect, 61